Student Handbook & Solutions Manual

Harry Nickla

ESSENTIALS OF
Genetics

Fourth Edition

William S. Klug
Michael R. Cummings

Prentice
Hall

Upper Saddle River, NJ 07458

Editor in Chief: Sheri Snavely
Project Manager: Karen Horton
Executive Managing Editor: Kathleen Schiaparelli
Assistant Managing Editor: Dinah Thong
Production Editor: Veronica Malone
Supplement Cover Manager: Paul Gourhan
Supplement Cover Designer: PM Workshop Inc.
Manufacturing Manager: Trudy Pisciotti
Photograph Credit: Jan-Michael Peters/Silke Hauf

© 2002 by Prentice-Hall, Inc.
Upper Saddle River, NJ 07458

Printed in the United States of America

10 9 8 7 6 5 4 3 2 1

ISBN   0-13-093338-4

Prentice-Hall International (UK) Limited, London
Prentice-Hall of Australia Pty. Limited, Sydney
Prentice-Hall Canada, Inc., Toronto
Prentice-Hall Hispanoamericana, S.A., Mexico City
Prentice-Hall of India Private Limited, New Delhi
Pearson Education Asia Pte. Ltd., Singapore
Prentice-Hall of Japan, Inc., Tokyo
Editora Prentice-Hall do Brazil, Ltda., Rio de Janeiro

Contents

Introduction: **Students, Read this Section First!**

How to Increase Your Chances of Success:

1. Attend Class
2. Read the Book
3. Do the Assigned Problems
4. Don't Cram
5. Study When There Are No Tests
6. Develop Confidence from Effort
7. Set Disciplined Study Goals
8. Learn Concepts
9. Be Careful with Old Exams
10. Don't "Second Guess"

The intent of this book is to help you understand introductory genetics as presented in the text **Essentials of Genetics** (4th edition) by Klug and Cummings. A first course in genetics can be a humbling experience for many students. It is possible that the lowest grades received in one's major, or even in one's undergraduate career, may be in genetics. It is not unusual for some students to become frustrated with their own inability to succeed in genetics. This frustration is felt by most teachers as they field most of the following student comments:

"I studied all the material but failed your test."

"I must have a mental block to it. I just don't get it. I just don't understand what you are asking."

"Where did you get that question? I didn't see anything like that in the book or in my notes."

"This is the first test I have **ever** failed."

"I helped three of my friends last night and I got the lowest grade."

"I am getting a 'D' in your course and I have never received less than a 'B' in my whole life."

"I stayed up all night studying for your exam and I still failed."

Similar to Algebra

Think back to the first time you encountered "word problems" in your first algebra class. How many times did you ask yourself, your parents, or to your teacher the following classic question?

> "I hate word problems, I just can't understand them, and why do I need to learn this anyway, I'll never use it?"

At that time you had two choices, to drop out and be afraid of problem-solving for the rest of your life (which unfortunately happens too often) or to regroup, seek help, strip away distractions, and focus in on learning something new and powerful. Because you are taking genetics, you probably succeeded in algebra, perhaps with difficulty at first, and you will probably succeed in genetics.

In algebra you were forced to convert something real and dynamic (two trains leaving at different times from different stations at different speeds, when do they meet?) to a somewhat abstract formula which can be applied to an infinite number of similar problems. In genetics you will

again learn something new. It will involve the conversion of something real and dynamic (genes, chromosomes, gamete formation, gene splicing, and evolution) to an array of general concepts (similar to mathematical formulas) which will allow you to predict the outcome of an infinite number of presently known and yet to be discovered phenomena relating to the origin and maintenance of life.

Mental Pictures and Symbols

When working almost any algebra word problem it is often helpful to make a simple drawing which relates, in space, the primary participants. From that drawing one can often predict or estimate a likely outcome. A mathematical formula and its solution provides the precise outcome. To understand genetics it is often helpful to make drawings of the participants, whether they be crosses (*Aa X Aa*), gametes 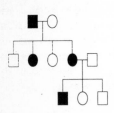 (*A* or *a*), or the interactions of molecules (anticodon with codon).

As with algebra, symbols used to represent a multitude of structures, movements, and interactions, are abstract, informative, and fundamental to understanding the discipline. It is the set of symbols and their interrelationships that comprise the concepts which make up the framework of genetics. Test questions and problems exemplify the concepts and may be completely unfamiliar to the student, nevertheless they refer directly to the basic concepts of genetics.

Attendance and Attention Are Mandatory

Many professors do not take attendance in lectures, therefore, it is likely that some students will opt to take a day off now and then. Unless those students are excellent readers and excellent students in general, continual absences will usually result in failure.

Remember how difficult it was to setup and understand the first algebra word problem on your own. It is likely that your ultimate source of understanding came from the course instructor. While using the text is important in your understanding of genetics, the teacher can walk you through the concepts and strategies much more efficiently than a text because a text is organized in a *sequential* manner. A good teacher can "cut and paste" an idea from here and there as needed.

To benefit from the wisdom of the instructor, the student must concentrate during the lecture session rather than sit, passively taking notes, assuming that the ideas can be figured out at a later date. Too often the student will not be able to relate to notes passively taken weeks before.

The instructor will not be able to cover all the material in the text. Parts will be emphasized while other areas may be omitted entirely. Since it is the instructor who writes and grades the tests, who is in a better position to prepare the students for those tests?

There is no magic formula for understanding genetics or any other discipline of significance. Learning anything, especially at the college level, requires time, patience, and confidence. First, a student must be willing to focus on the subject matter for an hour or so each day over the entire semester (quarter, trimester, etc.). Study time must be free of distractions and pressured by realistic goals.

The student must be patient and disciplined. It will be necessary to study when there are no assignments due and no tests looming.

The majority of successful students are willing to read the text ahead of the lecture material, spend time thinking about the concepts and examples, and work as many sample problems as possible. They study for a period of time, stop, then return to review the most difficult areas. They do not try to cram information into marathon study sessions a few nights before the examinations. While they may get away with that practice on occasion, more often than not, understanding the concepts in genetics requires more mature study habits and preparation.

2

Perhaps a Different Way of Thinking

Because the acquisition of problem-solving ability requires that students rely on new and important ways of seeing things rather than memorizing the book and notes, some students are faced with a difficult transition. Some students are more able to deal in the abstract, concept-oriented framework than others. Students who have typically relied on "pure memory" for their success will find a need to focus on concepts and problem-solving. They may struggle at first just as they may have struggled with the first word problem in algebra. But the reward for such struggle is intellectual growth. That's what college is supposed to stimulate. With such growth will come an increased ability to solve a variety of problems beyond genetics. Problem-solving is a process, a style, which can be applied to many disciplines. Few people are actually born with the touch of synthetic brilliance. Success comes from probing deeply in a few areas to see how problems are approached in a given discipline. Then, because problems are usually approached in a fairly consistent manner, a given problem-solving approach can often be applied to a variety of activities.

Ask Questions and Don't Tune Out!

When students ask questions, two things usually happen. First, an answer is provided which clarifies understanding. Second, the instructor is made aware of particularly problematic area. You will benefit, so will the instructor, and so will the shy student sitting next to you.

How to Study

Genetics is a science which involves symbols (A, b, p), structures (chromosomes, ribosomes, plasmids), and processes (meiosis, replication, translation) which interact in a variety of ways. Models describe the manner in which hereditary units are made, how they function, and how they are transmitted from parent to offspring. Because many parts of the models interact both in time and space, genetics cannot be viewed as a discipline filled with facts which should be memorized. Rather, one must be, or become, comfortable with seeking to understand not only the components of the models but also how the models work.

One can memorize the names and shapes of all the parts of an automobile engine, but without studying the interrelationships among the parts in time and space, one will have little understanding of the real nature of the engine. It takes time, work, and patience to see how an engine works and it will take time, work, and patience to understand genetics.

> **Time,**
> **Work,**
> **Patience**

Don't cram. A successful tennis player doesn't learn to play tennis overnight; therefore, you can't expect to learn genetics under the pressure of night-long cramming. It will be necessary for you to develop and follow a realistic study schedule for genetics as well as the other courses you are taking. It is important that you focus your study periods into intensive, but short sessions each day throughout the entire semester (quarter, trimester). Because genetics tests often require you to think "on the spot," it is very important that you get a good night's sleep before each test. Avoid caffeine in the evening before the test because a clear, rested, well-prepared mind will be required.

> **Study when there are no tests**

Study goals. The instruction of genetics is often divided into large conceptual units. A test usually follows each unit. It will be necessary for you to study genetics on a routine basis long before each test. To do so, set specific study goals. Adhere to these goals and don't let examinations in one course interfere with the study goals of another course. Notice that each course being taken is handled in the same way — study ahead of time and don't cram.

Tuesday

Study times:	Subject:
1st hour:	Genetics
2nd hour:	History
Recreation	
	Physics

Monday

Study times:	Subject:
1st hour:	Psychology
2nd hour:	Genetics
Recreation	
3rd hour:	History

Read ahead. You have been told that it is important to read the assigned material before attending lectures. This allows you to make full use of the information provided in the lecture and to concentrate on those areas which are unclear in the readings. An opportunity is often provided for asking questions. Your questions will be received much more favorably if you can say that after reading the book and listening to the lecture a particular point is still unclear. It is very likely that your question will be quickly dealt with to your benefit and the benefit of others in the class.

Develop a Realistic Schedule

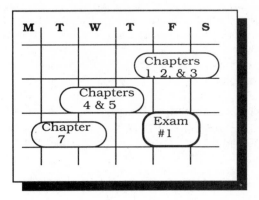

Develop a Plan for the Semester

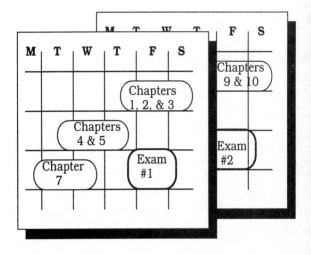

Work the assigned problems. The basic concepts of genetics are really quite straightforward but there are many examples which apply to these concepts. To help students adjust to the variety of examples and approaches to concepts, instructors often assign practice problems from the back of each chapter. If your instructor has assigned certain problems, finish working them *at least* one week before each examination. Before starting a set of problems, read the chapter carefully and consider the information presented in class.

Suggestions for working problems:

(1) Work the problem completely without looking at the answer or flipping back in the text.

(2) Check your answer in this book.

(3) If incorrect, work the problem again.

(4) If still incorrect, you don't understand the concept.

(5) Re-read your lecture notes and the text.

(6) Work the problem again.

(7) If you still don't understand the solution, mark it, and go to the next problem.

In your next study session, return to those problems which you have marked. Expect to make mistakes and learn from those mistakes. Sometimes what is difficult to see one day may be obvious the next day. If you are still having problems with a concept, schedule a meeting with your instructor. Usually the problem can be cleared up in a few minutes.

You will notice that in this book, I have presented the solution to each problem. I provide different ways of looking at some of the problems. Instructors often take a problem directly from those at the end of the chapters or they will modify an existing probem. Reversing the "direction" of a question is a common approach. Instead of giving characteristics of the parents and asking for characteristics of the offspring, the question may provide characteristics of the offspring and ask for particulars on the parents. Think as you work the problems.

Separate examples from concepts. As mentioned earlier, genetics boils down to a few (perhaps 15 to 20) basic concepts. However, there are many examples which apply to those concepts. Too often students have trouble separating examples from the concepts. Notice that in the "Sample Test" section in this book, I have made such separations clear. Examples allow you to picture, in concrete terms, various phenomena, but they don't exemplify each phenomenon or concept in its entirety.

Be careful when using old examinations. It is often customary for students to request or otherwise obtain old examinations from previous students. Such a practice is loaded with pitfalls. First, students often, albeit unconsciously, find themselves "second guessing" about questions on an upcoming examination. They forget that an examination usually only tests over a subset of the available information in a section. Therefore entire "conceptual areas" may be available for testing which have not appeared on recent exams.

Often the reproductions of old examinations are of poor quality (having been copied and passed around repeatedly) and it is difficult to determine whether the answer provided is correct. In addition, if a question has the same general structure as one on a previous examination, but is modified, students often provide an answer for the "old" question rather than the one being asked.

Granted, it is of value to see the format of each question and the general emphasis of previous examinations, but remember that each examination is potentially a new production capable of covering areas which have not been tested before. This is especially likely in a course such as genetics where the material changes very rapidly. **Don't try to figure out what will be asked.** Study all the material as well as possible.

Structure of this Book

The intent of this book is to help you understand the concepts of genetics as given in the text and most likely in the lectures, then to apply these concepts to the solution of all problems and questions at the ends of the chapters. Rather than merely provide you with the solutions to the problems, I have tried to walk you through each component of each question so that you can see where information is obtained and how it can be applied in the solution. At the beginning of each chapter is a section which relates particular problems to concept areas. This should help you practice certain conceptual areas as needed.

Vocabulary: Organization and listing of terms. Understanding the vocabulary of a discipline is essential to understanding the discipline. Throughout the text by Klug and Cummings you will find terms in bold print. Such terms generally refer to structures or substances, processes/methods, and concepts. I have separated these terms and *other important terms* into these categories.

Structures and Substances

Processes/Methods

Concepts

Those terms or concepts which require special explanation or are more complex or intimately related to other terms are denoted with a code (F2.1, F21.2, *etc.*) which refers you to the figures immediately following each **Concepts** section of this book. Use the listings as checklists to make certain that you understand the meaning of each term in each chapter. Also, by a given term's category, you can begin to understand whether it refers to a structure or substance, a process or method, or a more general concept. Notice that the various terms are not redefined. It is important that you use the Klug and Cummings text for the original definitions.

Understand the words and phrases of the discipline

Concepts. In the section *Vocabulary: Organization and Listing of Terms* you will find a section called *Concepts* after which there may be a simple sketch or two to help you focus a particular concept. Such sketches are oversimplifications and you should fill in the details by examining the textbook and the lecture notes.

Solved problems. Each of the problems at the end of each chapter is solved from a beginner's point of view. There are other features of this section. Some of the answers to the questions and problems will refer you to specific sections, usually specific tables and figures, of the Klug and Cummings (K/C) text. Be certain that you fully understand the solution to each of the questions suggested or assigned by your instructor.

Supplemental questions. A series of solved sample test questions supplement the questions provided in the text and help you determine your level of preparation. These sample test questions are located at the end of this book. Concepts relating to each question as well as common errors are presented in boxes before and after each answer.

Supplemental Questions

Concepts

Comprehensive Solution

Common errors

Chapter 1: An Introduction to Genetics

Concept Areas	*Corresponding Problems*
Definitions	2, 6, 7, 9, 10
Historical	1, 3, 4, 8
Information Flow	5

Vocabulary and Critical Issues

Historical

Prehistoric times

    domesticated animals

    cultivated plants

Greek Influence

    Hippocrates *(On the Seed)*

      "humors"

    Aristotle

      vital heat

Harvey

    epigenesis

Preformation

    homunculus

Cell theory

    spontaneous generation

Fixity of species

    Linnaeus

    Kolreuter

      hybridization

      parental types

      backcross

Evolution

    Darwin, Wallace

      The Origin of Species (1859)

      natural selection

Genetics

    Mendel (1866)

    Rediscovery (1900)

      Correns, de Vries, Von Tschermak

      Bateson

Chapter 1

Structures and Substances

Nucleic acids

    nucleotides

    DNA (deoxyribonucleic acid)

        Watson-Crick model

        double helix

            complementarity
                hydrogen bonds
            information storage
            replication
            mutation
            expression

        nitrogenous bases (ATGC)

    RNA (ribonucleic acid)

        uracil

    protein

Associated substances/structures

    amino acids

    messenger RNA

    ribosome

    ribosomal RNA

    transfer RNA

    protein

        enzymes

Processes/Methods

Transcription

Translation

Activation energy

Transmission genetics

    pedigree analysis

    cytological investigations

Cytogenetics

    chromosome theory of inheritance

    karyotypes

Molecular and genetic analysis

    recombinant DNA

    DNA biotechnology

    gene therapy

        Dolly

Population Genetics

Genetic structure of populations

Basic research

Applied research

    eugenics

        Galton

            positive

            negative

    euphenics

    agriculture

        "Green Revolution"

        Borlaug

    medicine

        human genetic engineering

        immunogenetics

        human genome project

Concepts

Trinity of molecular genetics

Genetic code and RNA triplets

    genetic code

    transcription

    translated (translation)

Investigative approaches

Genetics and society

Age of genetics

F1.1. Sketch of the relationships among major components of the *Trinity of Molecular Genetics*

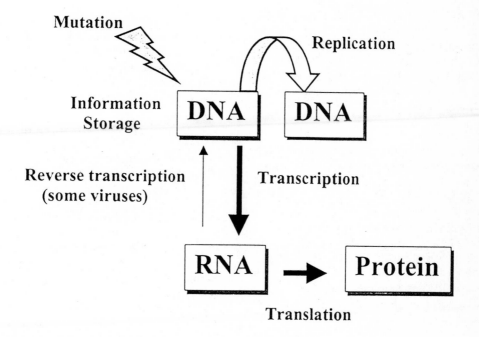

Solutions to Problems and
Discussion Questions

1. Both were concerned with subjects of the reproduction, heredity, the origin of humans, and the shifting of interest from religious mythology to philosophical and scientific inquiries. Hippocrates argued that male semen is formed in various parts of the body (healthy or diseased) and transported through blood vessels to the testicles. Such "humors" carried the hereditary traits. Thus the theory of pangenesis was formed. Aristotle was critical of pangenesis because it did not explain the appearance of features which skipped generations. Aristotle suggested that semen contained a vital heat which could produce offspring in the form of the parents.

2. *Epigenesis* refers to the theory that organisms are derived from the assembly and reorganization of substances in the egg which eventually lead to the development of the adult. *Preformationism* is a 17th century theory which states that the sex cells (eggs or sperm) contain miniature adults, called homunculi, which grow in size to become the adult. Each postulates a fundamental differnce in the manner in which organisms develop from hereditary determiners.

3. Darwin was aware of the physical and physiological diversity of members within and among various species. He was aware that varieties of organisms could be developed through selective breeding (domestication), that a species is not a fixed entity, and that while certain groups of organisms could be hybridized, other groups could not. He was aware of conflicts between religious views and the fossil record. He understood geology, geography, and biology and that organisms tend to leave more offspring than the environment can support.

4. Darwin's theory of natural selection proposed that more offspring are produced than can survive, and that in the competition for survival, those with favorable variations survive. Over many generations this will produce a change in the genetic make-up of populations if the favorable variations are inherited. Darwin did not understand the nature of heredity and variation which led him to lean toward older theories of pangenesis and inheritance of acquired characteristics.

5. Genes, linear sequences of nucleotides, usually exert their influence by producing proteins through the process of transcription and translation. The "Trinity of Molecular Genetics" is illustrated in F1.1 of this book. Genes are the functional units of heredity. They associate, sometimes with proteins, to form chromosomes. During the cell cycle, chromosomes and therefore genes, are duplicated by a variety of enzymes so that daughter cells inherit copies of the parental hereditary information. Genes of eukaryotes are composed of DNA.

6. *Transmission* genetics is the most classical approach in which the patterns of inheritance are studied through selective matings or the results of natural matings. Mendel observed results from precisely-defined matings and provided models based on transmission genetics.

A second approach involves physical, traditionally microscopic (light and electron), examination of chromosomes. With the discovery of mitotic and meiotic processes, and the knowledge that genes are located on chromosomes, much interest centers on the *cytological investigation* of chromosomes.

Molecular and biochemical analysis of the genetic material has recently evolved into one of the most exciting and rapidly growing subdisciplines of genetics. Originating in the early 1940s with studies of bacteria and viruses, much information as to the nature of gene expression, regulation, and replication has been provided. *Recombinant DNA technology* has had a significant impact in this area as well as others.

In *population* genetics, the interest is in the behavior of genes in groups of organisms (populations) often with an interest in the factors which change gene frequencies in time and space. Hence population geneticists are often interested in the process of evolution.

7. *Basic* research involves the study of the fundamental mechanisms of genetics as described in the answer to question #6 above. *Applied* research makes use of the information provided by basic research. Many applications in agriculture and medicine are described in the text.

8. Norman Borlaug applied Mendelian principles of hybridization and trait selection to the development of superior varieties of wheat. Such varieties are now grown in many countries, including Mexico, and have helped maintain the world supply of food. This change in worldwide agricultural food production has been called the "Green Revolution."

9. *Positive eugenics* encouraged parents displaying favorable characteristics to have large families while *negative eugenics* attempted to restrict reproduction for parents displaying unfavorable characteristics. *Euphenics* refers to medical genetic intervention designed to reduce the impact of defective genes on individuals.

10. In the last 50 years human transmission, cytological and molecular genetics have provided an understanding of many aspects of both plant and animal biology including development of pest resistant crops and identification of hazardous organisms in our food (*E. coli* for example). In addition, much has been learned about many human diseases. There is promise that a certain amount of human suffering will be minimized by the application of genetics to crop production (disease resistance, protein content, growth conditions) and medicine. Major medical areas of activity include genetic counseling, gene mapping and identification, disease diagnosis, and genetic engineering.

Chapter 2: Mitosis and Meiosis

Concept Areas	Corresponding Problems
General	1, 7, 16, 19, 20
Homologous Chromosomes	2, 3, 6, 7
Mitosis	4, 5, 8, 9, 10, 12
Meiosis	11, 12, 13, 14, 15, 16, 17, 18, 19

Vocabulary and Critical Issues

Structures and Substances

Cell structure

   mitosis

   meiosis

     gametes

     spores

   plasma membrane

   cell wall

     cellulose

   capsule

   cell coat

     AB antigens

     MN antigens

     histocompatibility antigens

     receptor molecules

   nucleus, nucleoid region

     genetic material (DNA/protein)

     chromatin

     chromosomes

     nucleolus

       nucleolar organizer (NOR)

       rRNA

   cytoplasm

     organelles

     colloidal

     cytosol

       cytoskeleton

         microtubules, microfilaments

     endoplasmic reticulum

     ribosomes

     mitochondria

     chloroplasts (photosynthesis)

     basal body

     centrioles

     spindle fibers

Chromosomes

   centromere, p arm, q arm

   metacentric

submetacentric

acrocentric

telocentric

karyotype

sex-determining chromosomes

Mitosis

zygotes

centrosome, centriole

spindle fibers

chromatid

locus

centromere, kinetochore

sister chromatids (non-sister)

metaphase plate

molecular motors

karyokinesis

cell plate

middle lamella

cell furrow

Meiosis

bivalent
tetrad
dyad
monad

chiasma (chiasmata)
synaptonemal complex
lateral element

Gametogenesis

testes

spermatogonium
primary spermatocyte
secondary spermatocyte
spermatid
spermatozoa (sperm)

ovary

oogonium
primary oocyte
secondary oocyte

first polar body
ootid
second polar body
ova (ovum)

Chromatin/chromosomes

folded fiber model

Processes/Methods

Gametes, spores

Mitosis

cell cycle

cytokinesis (middle lamella)

interphase

S phase

G_1 and G_2

M phase

prophase
prometaphase
metaphase
anaphase
telophase

Regulation

significance

G_0

G_1/S checkpoint

G_2/M checkpoint

M checkpoint

cdc2, kinase

cyclins

p53

tumor-suppressor gene

Meiosis

reduction division

equational

prophase I

leptonema

zygonema

homology search

rough pairing

pachynema(synapsis)

crossing over

diplonema

diakinesis (terminalization)

metaphase I
anaphase I
telophase I

prophase II
metaphase II
anaphase II
telophase II

Spermatogenesis

Spermiogenesis

Oogenesis

first meiotic division (at ovulation)

second meiotic division (at fertilization)

Fertilization

Sexual reproduction

reshuffles chromosomes

provides for crossing over

Sporophyte

Gametophyte

Concepts

Biparental inheritance

Endosymbiont hypothesis

Homologous chromosomes (F2.2)

diploid number (2n) (F2.1)

loci (F2.2)

haploid genome (haploid number, n) (F2.2)

alleles (F2.2)

Mitosis (T2.1)

identical daughters

equivalent genetic information

Meiosis (F2.3)

   segregation

   independent assortment

     disjunction

     non-disjunction

   produces gametes or spores

reshuffles genetic combinations
   (chromosomes)

genetic recombination (crossing over)

production of variation

Fertilization

   reconstitution of genetic material

F2.1. Diagram showing the relationships among stages of interphase chromosomes, chromosome number, and chromosome structure in an organism with a diploid chromosome number of 4 (2n = 4). There are two pairs of chromosomes, one large metacentric, one smaller metacentric. Individual chromosomes cannot be seen at interphase, therefore, the drawings represent chromosomes *as if* they could be individually viewed.

Interphase

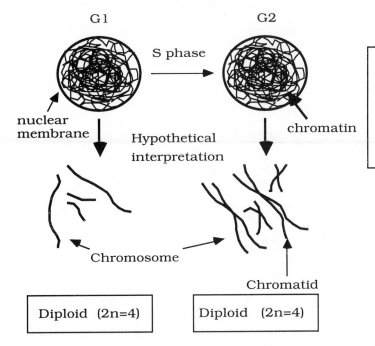

G1

G2

S phase

nuclear
membrane

Hypothetical
interpretation

chromatin

Notice that in mitosis, there is no change in chromosome number even though the DNA content increases (doubles) in each nucleus during the S phase. The chromosomes become doubled structures as the result of S phase.

Chromosome

Chromatid

Diploid (2n=4)

Diploid (2n=4)

F2.2. Important nomenclature referring to chromosomes and genes in an organism where the diploid chromosome number is 4 (2n = 4). There are two pairs of chromosomes, one large metacentric, and one smaller metacentric. Sister chromatids are *identical* to each other, while homologous chromosomes are *similar* to each other in terms of overall size, centromere position, function, and other factors as described in your text.

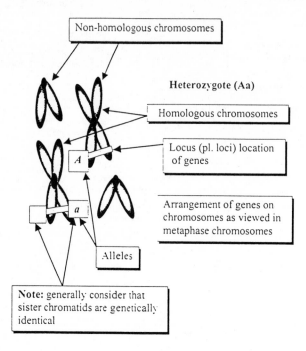

T2.1. Illustration of the relationship between chromosome number and stages of the mitotic cycle.

Cell cycle stage	Chromosome number	
	humans	**fruit flies**
Interphase	2n = 46	2n = 8
G1	2n = 46	2n = 8
S	2n = 46	2n = 8
G2	2n = 46	2n = 8
Mitosis		
Prophase	2n = 46	2n = 8
Prometaphase	2n = 46	2n = 8
Metaphase	2n = 46	2n = 8
Anaphase	2n = 46	2n = 8
Telophase	2n = 46	2n = 8

F2.3. Illustrations of chromosomes of meiotic and mitotic cells in an organism with a chromosome number of 4 (2n = 4).

Meiosis

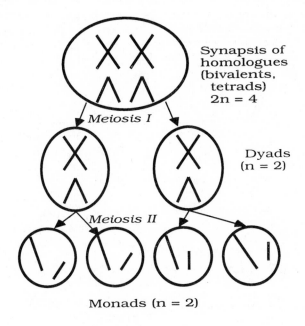

Synapsis of homologues (bivalents, tetrads) 2n = 4

Meiosis I

Dyads (n = 2)

Meiosis II

Monads (n = 2)

Mitosis

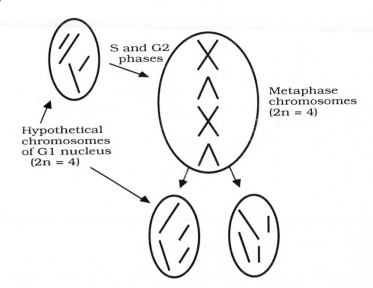

S and G2 phases

Hypothetical chromosomes of G1 nucleus (2n = 4)

Metaphase chromosomes (2n = 4)

Solutions to Problems and Discussion Questions

1.

(a) During interphase of the cell cycle (mitotic and meiotic), chromosomes are not condensed and are in a genetically active, spread out, form. In this condition, chromosomes are not visible as individual structures under the microscope (light or electron). See F2.1 for a sketch of what *chromatin* might look like. Chromatin contains the genetic material which is responsible for maintaining hereditary information (from one cell to daughter cells and from one generation to the next) and production of the phenotype.

(b) The *nucleolus* (*pl. nucleoli*) is a structure which is produced by activity of the nucleolar organizer region in eukaryotes. Composed of ribosomal RNA and coding DNA, it is the site for the production of ribosomes. Some nuclei have more than one *nucleolus*. Nucleoli are not present during mitosis or meiosis because in the condensed state of chromosomes, there is little or no RNA synthesis.

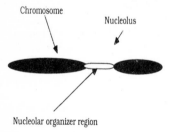

Chromosome

Nucleolus

Nucleolar organizer region

(c) The *ribosome* is the structure where various RNAs, enzymes, and other molecular species assemble the primary sequence of a protein. That is, amino acids are placed in order as specified by messenger RNA. Ribosomes are relatively non-specific in that virtually any ribosome can be used in the translation of any mRNA. The structure and function of the ribosome will be described in greater detail in later chapters of the *Essentials* text.

(d) The *mitochondrion* (*pl. mitochondria*) is a membrane-bound structure located in the cytoplasm of eukaryotic cells. It is the site of oxidative phosphorylation and production of relatively large amounts of ATP. It is the trapping of energy in ATP which drives many of the important metabolic processes in living systems.

(e) The *centriole* is a cytoplasmic structure involved (through the formation of spindle fibers) in the migration of chromosomes during mitosis and meiosis.

(f) The *centromere* serves is a point of kinetochore assembly and serves as an attachment point for sister chromatids (see F2.1). The centromere divides during mitosis and meiosis II, thus aiding in the partitioning of chromosomal material to daughter cells. Failure of centromeres or spindle fibers to function properly may result in nondisjunction.

2. One of the most important concepts to be gained from this chapter is the relationship which exists among chromosomes in a single cell. Chromosomes which are homologous share many properties including:

overall length; look carefully at F2.1 and F2.2 to see that each cell prior to anaphase I contains two chromosomes of approximately the same overall length.

position of the centromere (metacentric, submetacentric, acrocentric, telocentric); Again, look carefully at F2.1 and F2.2, and the *Essentials* text. Notice that in each, if there is one metacentric chromosome, there will be another metacentric chromosome.

banding patterns; Look carefully at the *Essentials* text and notice how similar the banding patterns are of the homologous (side by side) chromosomes. Notice also that sister chromatids have identical banding patterns as would be expected since sister chromatids are, with the exception of mutation, identical copies of each other. We would expect that homologous chromosomes would have banding patterns which are very similar (but not identical) because homologous chromosomes are genetically similar but not genetically identical.

type and location of genes; Notice in F2.2 that a *locus* signifies the location of a gene along a chromosome. What that really means is that for each characteristic specified by a gene, such as blood type, eye color, skin pigmentation, there are genes located along chromosomes. The *order* of such loci is identical in homologous chromosomes, but the genes themselves, while being in the same order, may not be identical.

Look carefully at the inset (box) in the upper right portion of F2.2 and see that there are alternative forms of genes, *A* and *a*, at the same location along the chromosome. *A* and *a* are located at the same place and specify the same *characteristic* (eye color for example) but there are slightly different manifestations of eye color (*brown* vs. *blue* for example). Just as an individual may inherit gene *A* from the father and gene *a* from the mother, each zygote inherits one homologue of each pair from the father and one homologue of each pair from the mother.

autoradiographic pattern; homologous chromosomes tend to replicate during the same time of S phase.

Diploidy is a term often used in conjunction with the symbol *2n*. It means that both members of a homologous pair of chromosomes are present. Refer to F2.1 in this book. Notice that during mitosis, the normal chromosome complement is 2n or diploid. In humans, the diploid chromosome number is 46 while in *Drosophila* it is 8. *Essentials*-Tab.2.1 lists the *haploid* chromosome number for a variety of species. Notice that in man and flies, the haploid chromosome number is one-half the diploid number. This applies to other organisms as well. However, it is very important to realize that *haploidy* specifically refers to the fact that each haploid cell contains *one chromosome of each homologous pair of chromosomes*. Compare the nuclear contents of a spermatid and a cell at zygonema in the *Essentials* text. Note that each spermatid contains one member of each of the original chromosome pairs (seen at zygonema). Haploidy is usually symbolized as *n*. The change from a diploid (2n) to haploid (n) occurs during *reduction division* when tetrads become dyads during meiosis I. Referring to the number of human chromosomes, the primary spermatocyte (2n=46) becomes two secondary spermatocytes each with n = 23.

3. As you examine the criteria for *homology* in question #2 above, you can see that overall length and centromere position are but two factors required for homology. Most importantly, genetic content in non-homologous chromosomes is expected to be quite different. Other factors including banding pattern and time of replication during S phase would also be expected to vary among non-homologous chromosomes.

4. Because much of Chapter 2 deals with mitosis, it would be best to deal with this question by reading the sections which cover mitosis in the *Essentials* text. Understanding mitosis and all the related terms is essential for an understanding of genetics. There are several sample test questions at the end of this book which will help you determine your understanding of mitosis. Refer to T2.1 and note that chromosome number does not change during mitosis.

5. The first sentence tells you that 2n = 16 and it is a question about mitosis. Since each chromosome in prophase is doubled (having gone through an S phase) and is visible at the end of prophase, there should be 32 chromatids. Because the centromeres divide, and what were previously sister chromatids migrate to opposite poles during anaphase, there should be 16 chromosomes moving to each pole. If you refer to F2.1 and the *Essentials* text you will see an example which will help illustrate these points.

6. Refer to the *Essentials* text (Figure 2-3) for an explanation. Notice the different anaphase shapes in the figures. Chromosomes are classified as *metacentric*, *submetacentric*, *acrocentric*, or *telocentric* on the basis of centromere location.

7. Because of a cell wall around the plasma membrane in plants, a cell plate, which was laid down during anaphase, becomes the middle lamella where primary and secondary layers of the cell wall are deposited.

8. Carefully read the section dealing with mitosis in *Essentials*. The mitotic cell cycle is separated into two major portions: interphase (G_1, S, G_2) and mitosis. Refer to F2.1 and figures in the *Essentials* text for information pertaining to the interphase. Refer to the *Essentials* text for a diagram of mitosis. Notice that, in contrast to meiosis, there is no pairing of homologous chromosomes in mitosis and the chromosome number does not change (see T2.1). Cell cycle control is achieved by the interaction of cyclin dependent kinase (cdk) in conjunction with cyclins. There are at least three major checkpoints; G_1/S, G_2/M, and M (in mitosis).

9. There are three primary checkpoints in the cell cycle. The G1/S checkpoint monitors cell size and DNA damage. The G2/M checkpoint monitors physiological conditions in the cell and determines the extent of DNA replication and repair. The M checkpoint monitors chromosome attachment and positioning.

10. p53 plays a role in regulating the G1 to S transition. It is a tumor suppressor. Mutations cause a lack of control over the cell cycle and cancer often follows.

11. Not necessarily. If crossing over occurred in meiosis I, then the chromatids in the secondary oocyte are not identical. Once they separate during meiosis II, unlike chromatids reside in the ootid and the second polar body.

12. Compared with mitosis, meiosis provides for a reduction in chromosome number, and an opportunity for exchange of genetic material between homologous chromosomes. In mitosis there is no change in chromosome number (see T2.1) or kind in the two daughter cells, whereas in meiosis, numerous potentially different haploid (n) cells are produced. During oogenesis, only one of the four meiotic products is functional; however, four of the four meiotic products of spermatogenesis are potentially functional.

13. (a) *Synapsis* is the point-by-point pairing of homologous chromosomes during prophase of meiosis I.

(b) *Bivalents* are those structures formed by the synapsis of homologous chromosomes. In other words, there are two chromosomes (four chromatids) which make up a bivalent. If an organism has a diploid chromosome number of 46, then there will be 23 bivalents in meiosis I.

(c) *Chiasmata* is the plural form of chiasma and refers to the structure, when viewed microscopically, of crossed chromatids. Notice in the figures of the *Essentials* text the exchange of chromatid pieces in diplonema and diakinesis.

(d) *Crossing over* is the exchange of genetic material between chromatids. Also called recombination, it is a method of providing genetic variation through the breaking and rejoining of chromatids. Notice in *Essentials* the mixing of genetic material along the length of the chromatids.

(e) *Chromomeres* are patches of chromatin which look different from neighboring patches along the length of a chromosome.

(f) Examine F2.1 in this book. Notice that *sister chromatids* are "post-S phase" structures of replicated chromosomes. Sister chromatids are genetically identical (except where mutations have occurred) and are attached at same centromere. Identify the sister chromatids in figures in the *Essentials* text. Note that sister chromatids separate from each other during anaphase of mitosis and anaphase II of meiosis.

(g) Tetrads are synapsed homologous chromosomes thereby composed of four chromatids. There are as many tetrads as the haploid chromosome number.

(h) Actually, each tetrad is made of two dyads which separate from each other during anaphase I of meiosis. Dyads are composed of two chromatids joined by a centromere.

(i) At anaphase II of meiosis, the centromeres divide and sister chromatids go to opposite poles forming monads.

14. Look carefully at F2.3 in this book and notice that, for a cell with 4 chromosomes, there are two tetrads, each comprised of a homologous pair of chromosomes.

(a) If there are 16 chromosomes there should be 8 tetrads.

(b) Also note that, after meiosis I and in the second meiotic prophase there are as many dyads as there are *pairs* of chromosomes. There will be 8 dyads.

(c) Because the monads migrate to opposite poles during meiosis II (from the separation of dyads) there should be 8 monads migrating to *each* pole.

15. Examine the *Essentials* text and the figures below. Notice that major differences include the sex in which each occurs, and that the distribution of cytoplasm is unequal in oogenesis but considered to be equal in the products of spermatogenesis. Chromosomal behavior is the same in spermatogenesis and oogenesis except that the nuclear activity in oogenesis is "off-center," thereby producing first and second polar bodies by unequal cytoplasmic division. Each spermatogonium and primary spermatocyte produces four spermatids, whereas each oogonium and primary oocyte produces one ootid. Because early development occurs in the absence of outside nutrients, it is likely that the unequal distribution of cytoplasm in oogenesis evolved to provide sufficient information and nutrients to the ovum to support development until the transcriptional activities of the zygotic nucleus begin to provide products.

Polar bodies probably represent non-functional by-products of such evolution.

Spermatogenesis

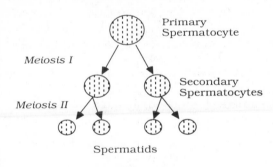

Oogenesis

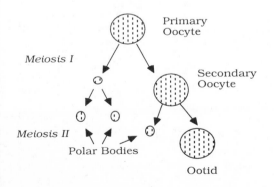

16. In meiosis, various chromosomal arrangements are possible because of random alignment of homologous chromosomes at metaphase I. In addition, crossing over, which introduces additional variation, is virtually absent in mitotic processes.

17. This question specifically tests your understanding of meiosis and the behavior of chromosomes during anaphase. In this question you must first visualize the alignment of the three homologous chromosome pairs C1,C2, M1,M2, and S1,S2 in mitosis (no synapsis of homologues) as compared with the alignment in meiosis.

(a)

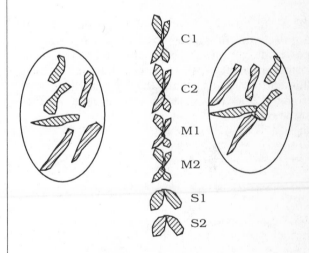

The two daughter cells will have the same chromosomes after mitosis

(b)

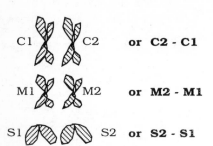

C1   C2   **or C2 - C1**

M1   M2   **or M2 - M1**

S1   S2   **or S2 - S1**

 Paternally derived

 Maternally derived

Notice that there are no constraints on the alignment of different pairs of homologous chromosomes, therefore one could list 8 configurations.

c) Because of the independent assortment of non-homologous chromosomes at anaphase I and the fact that anaphase II separates sister (identical) chromatids, there will be eight different meiotic (haploid) products. This answer can be derived from the 2^n formula where n is the haploid chromosome number.

18. There would be 16 combinations possible.

19. In plants, one often speaks of "alternation of generations" in which the life cycle alternates between the diploid sporophyte and the haploid gametophyte stages. Meiosis and fertilization bridge the sporophyte and gametophyte generations.

20. The cytological origin of the mitotic chromosome (and the meiotic chromosome for that matter) appears during the prophase through a condensation of the dispersed chromatin fibers present during interphase. During interphase, chromatin consists of invisible threads (under light microscopy) of DNA associated with histones. In this form, DNA can function in transcription and replication. Visible mitotic chromosomes appear when each chromosome coils and condenses according to the current *folded fiber model.*

21. Often circular, the bacterial chromosome is replicated in a bidirectional manner starting at a single point of initiation. Eukaryotic chromosomes are linear and have multiple points of replication initiation. Within these points of initiation, replication is bidirectional also. The products of eukaryotic chromosome replication (sister chromatids) are held together by a centromere.

22. The two smaller chromosomes are probably homologous and would be similar for the following characteristics: function, arrangement of genes, time of replication during the S phase, banding, *etc.*

Chapter 3: Mendelian Genetics

Concept Areas	Corresponding Problems
Mendelism	4, 9, 10, 12, 23
Monohybrid Crosses	1, 2, 3, 5
Dihybrid Crosses	6, 7, 8, 13, 16, 26, 28
Other Crosses	15, 22, 23, 24, 25, 27
Statistical Aspects, Probability	17, 18, 19, 20, 21
Chromosome (Gene) Behavior	14
Homologous Chromosomes	11

Vocabulary and Critical Issues

Historical

Mendelian Genetics (Gregor Mendel) - 1866

> *Pisum sativum*

>> units of inheritance (particulate)

> Rediscovery (1900)

>> Hugo DeVries

>> Karl Correns

>> Erich Tschermak

> Walter Flemming

> Walter Sutton

> Theodor Boveri

Structures and Substances

Unit factors

Genes

Alleles (also multiple alleles)

Locus

Processes/Methods

Transmission genetics

> monohybrid cross

>> maternal parent

>> paternal parent

> reciprocal cross

Punnett squares

> test cross

> parental generation (P_1)

> first filial generation (F_1)

> second filial generation (F_2)

> ratios

>> 3:1

>> 9:3:3:1

> product law

> sum law

2^n (n = haploid chromosome number)

dihybrid cross (two-factor cross)

trihybrid cross (three-factor cross)

forked-line (branch diagram) method

Statistical testing (analysis)

proportions

sample size

chance deviation

random fluctuations

null hypothesis (H_o)

measured values

predicted values

chi-square analysis (χ^2)

degrees of freedom

probability value (p)

reject the null hypothesis

fail to reject the null hypothesis

0.05 probability value

Pedigree

sibs, sibship line

monozygotic (identical) twins

dizygotic (fraternal) twins

proband

Concepts

Mendel's Postulates

unit factors in pairs (F3.1)

dominance/recessiveness (F3.1)

segregation

independent assortment

Symbolism (F3.2)

phenotype

genotype

homozygous (homozygote)

heterozygous (heterozygote)

Continuous variation

Discontinuous variation

Probabilty

Statistical testing

F 3.1. Illustration of the union of maternal and paternal genes (*A* and *a*) to give two genes in the zygote. Mendelian "unit factors" occur in pairs in diploid organisms. Dominant genes are often given the upper case letter as the symbol while the lower case letter is often used to symbolize the recessive gene.

It is important to see that each parent contributes one chromosome of each type (homologue) and thus one gene of each gene pair.

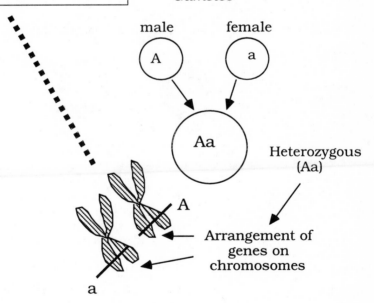

F3.2. It is important to see that in the drawing below there are four variations, but only two characteristics (shape and color). When developing symbols for gene pairs, keep upper and lower case letters (or other compatible scheme) *of the same letter* to represent genes of the same characteristic.

Two characteristics but a
total of four alternatives

Two Characteristics

Shape (round, wrinkled)
Color (black, white)

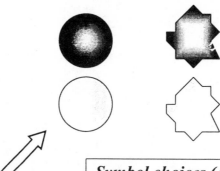

Selection of appropriate
symbols is critical

Symbol choices (examples)

W = **round** *w* = **wrinkled**
(assuming round is dominant to
wrinkled)

B = **black** *b* = **white**
(assuming black is dominant to white)

Chapter 3

Solutions to Problems and Discussion Questions

1. Several points surface in the first sentence of this question. First, two alternatives (black and white) of one characteristic (coat color) are being described, therefore it is a monohybrid condition (Fig.3.1).

Second, are the guinea pigs in the parental generation (P_1) homozygous or heterozygous? Notice in the introductory sentence, just after PROBLEMS AND DISCUSSION QUESTIONS, there is the statement "members of the P_1 generation are homozygous..."

Third, which is dominant, *black* or *white*? Note that all the offspring are black, therefore black can be considered dominant. The second sentence of the problem verifies that a monohybrid cross is involved because of the 3/4 black and 1/4 white distribution in the offspring. Knowing that genes occur in pairs in diploid organisms, one can write the genotypes and the phenotypes as follows:

P_1:

Phenotypes: Black   X   White

Genotypes: *WW*   *ww*

Gametes: *W*   *w*

F_1:   *Ww* (Black)

F_1 X F_1:

Phenotypes: Black   X   Black

Genotypes: *Ww*   *Ww*

Gametes: *W*   *w*   *W*   *w*

(combine as in *Essentials*)

F_2:

Phenotypes: Black   Black Black White

Genotypes: *WW*   *Ww*   *Ww*   *ww*

---

2. Start out with the following gene symbols:

A = normal (not albino),

a = albino.

Since albinism is inherited as a recessive trait, genotypes *AA* and *Aa* should produce the normal phenotype, while *aa* will give albinism.

(a) The parents are both normal, therefore they could be either *AA* or *Aa*. The fact that they produce an albino child requires that each parent provides an *a* gene to the albino child; thus the parents must both be heterozygous(*Aa*).

(b) To start out, the normal male could have either the *AA* or *Aa* genotype. The female must be *aa*. Since all the children are normal, one would consider the male to be *AA* instead of *Aa*. However, the male *could* be *Aa*. Under that circumstance, the likelihood of having six children, all normal, is 1/64.

3. *Unit factors in Pairs, Dominance and Recessiveness, Segregation*

4. *Pisum sativum* is easy to cultivate. It is naturally self-fertilizing, but it can be crossbred. It has several visible features (*e.g.*, tall or short, red flowers or white flowers) which are consistent under a variety of environmental conditions yet contrast due to genetic circumstances. Seeds could be obtained from local merchants.

5. With many problems, students often have trouble getting started in the right direction and seeing the problem through to the necessary conclusions. First, read the entire question and see that you are to determine (1) the pattern of inheritance for "checkered and plain," and (2) the gene symbols and genotypes of all the parents and offspring. Notice that there is reference to one characteristic, *pattern*, with two alternatives, checkered vs. plain. We should consider this to be a monohybrid condition unless complications arise.

Assignment of symbols:

P = checkered; *p* = plain. Checkered is tentatively assigned the dominant function because in a casual examination of the data, especially cross (b), we see that checkered types are more likely to be produced than plain types.

Cross (a):

PP X PP or *PP X Pp*

Cross (b):

PP X pp

This assignment seems reasonable because among 38 offspring, no plain types are produced. In addition, we would expect all the F_1 progeny to be heterozygous.

Cross (c):

Because all the offspring from this cross are plain, there is no doubt that the genotype of both parents is *pp*.

Genotypes of all individuals:

		F_1 *Progeny*	
P, Cross		*Checkered*	*Plain*
(a) *PP X PP*		*PP*	
(b) *PP X pp*		*Pp*	
(c) *pp X pp*			*pp*

In a mating of the F1 X F1 from cross (b), one would expect a 3:1 ratio of checkered to plain as shown below:

	P	*p*
P	*PP*	*Pp*
p	*Pp*	*pp*

6. In the first sentence you are told that there are two *characteristics* which are being studied; seed shape and cotyledon color. Expect, therefore, this to be a dihybrid situation with *two gene pairs* involved. One also sees the possible alternatives of these two characteristics: *seed shape*; wrinkled vs. round; *cotyledon color*; green vs. yellow. After reading the second sentence you can predict that the gene for round seeds is dominant to that for wrinkled seeds and that the gene for yellow cotyledons is dominant to the gene for green cotyledons.

Symbolism:

w = wrinkled seeds g = green cotyledons

W = round seeds G = yellow cotyledons

P_1:

WWGG X wwgg

Parents are considered to be homozygous for two reasons. First, in the introductory sentence, just after PROBLEMS AND DISCUSSION QUESTIONS, there is the statement "members of the P_1 generation are homozygous..." Second, notice that the only offspring are those with round seeds and yellow cotyledons.

Gametes produced: One member of each gene pair is "segregated" to each gamete.

WWGG   wwgg

(WG)   (wg)

F_1:   WwGg

F_1 X F_1:

WwGg X WwGg

Gametes produced: Under conditions of independent assortment, there will be four (2^n, where n = number of heterozygous gene pairs) different types of gametes produced by each parent.

Punnett Square

	WG	Wg	wG	wg
WG	WWGG	WWGg	WwGG	WwGg
Wg	WWGg	WWgg	WwGg	Wwgg
wG	WwGG	WwGg	wwGG	wwGg
wg	WwGg	Wwgg	wwGg	wwgg

Collecting the phenotypes according to the dominance scheme presented above, gives the following:

9/16   W_G_   round seeds, yellow cotyledons

3/16   W_gg   round seeds, green cotyledons

3/16   wwG_   wrinkled seeds, yellow cotyledons

1/16   wwgg   wrinkled seeds, green cotyledons

Notice that a dash (_) is used where, because of dominance, it makes no difference as to the dominance/recessive status of the allele.

Forked, or branch diagram:

Seed shape	Cotyledon color	Phenotypes
3/4 round	3/4 yellow	9/16 round, yellow
	1/4 green	3/16 round, green
1/4 wrinkled	3/4 yellow	3/16 wrinkled, yellow
	1/4 green	1/16 wrinkled, green

7. Symbolism as before:

w = wrinkled seeds	g = green cotyledons
W = round seeds	G = yellow cotyledons

Examine each characteristic (seed shape vs. cotyledon color) separately.

(a) Notice a 3:1 ratio for seed shape, therefore Ww X Ww; and no green cotyledons, therefore GG X GG or GG X Gg. Putting the two characteristics together gives

$WwGG$	X	$WwGG$
	or	
$WwGG$	X	$WwGg$

(b) Notice a 1:1 ratio for seed shape (8/16 wrinkled and 8/16 round) and a 3:1 ratio for cotyledon color (12/16 yellow and 4/16 green). Therefore the answer is

$$wwGg \ X \ WwGg.$$

(c) This is a typical 1:1:1:1 test cross (or back-cross) ratio:

$$WwGg \ X \ wwgg$$

8. A test cross involves mating an organism of unknown genotype with a fully homozygous recessive organism. In Problem #7, (c) is a test cross.

9. Because *independent assortment* may be defined as one gene pair segregating independently of another gene pair, one would need at least two gene pairs in order to demonstrate independent assortment, as is the case in Problem #7.

10. Mendel's four postulates are related to the diagram below.

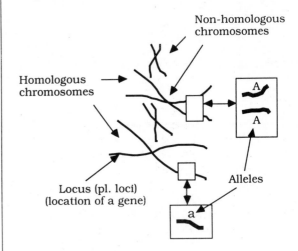

1. Factors occur in pairs. Notice A and a.

2. Some genes have dominant and recessive alleles. Notice A and a.

3. Alleles segregate from each other during gamete formation. When homologous chromosomes separate from each other at anaphase I, alleles will go to opposite poles of the meiotic apparatus.

4. One gene pair separates independently from other gene pairs. Different gene pairs on the same homologous pair of chromosomes (if far apart) or on non-homologous chromosomes will separate independently from each other during meiosis.

11. Carefully re-read the answer to Question #2 in Chapter #2. Briefly, the factors which specify chromosomal homology are the following:

type and location of genes

overall length

position of the centromere

banding patterns

autoradiographic pattern

12. Homozygosity refers to a condition where both genes of a pair are the same (i.e. *AA* or *GG* or *hh*), whereas heterozygosity refers to the condition where members of a gene pair are different (i.e. *Aa* or *Gg* or *Bb*). Homozygotes produce only one type of gamete whereas heterozygotes will produce 2^n types of gametes where n = number of heterozygous gene pairs (assuming independent assortment).

13. There are two characteristics presented here, body color and wing length. First, assign meaningful gene symbols.

Body color	Wing length
E = grey body color	V = long wings
e = ebony body color	v = vestigial wings

(a)

P_1:

  EEVV X eevv

F_1: *EeVv* (grey, long)

F_2:

This will be the result of a Punnett Square with 16 boxes as in *Essentials*-Fig.3.7.

Phenotypes	Ratio	Genotypes	Ratio
grey , long	9/16	*EEVV*	1/16
		EEVv	2/16
		EeVV	2/16
		EeVv	4/16
grey, vestigial	3/16	*EEvv*	1/16
		Eevv	2/16
ebony, long	3/16	*eeVV*	1/16
		eeVv	2/16
ebony, vestigial	1/16	*eevv*	1/16

(b)

P_1:

  EEvv X eeVV

  F_1: It is important to see that the results from this cross will be exactly the same as those in part (a) above. The only difference is that the recessive genes are coming from both parents, rather than from one parent only as in (a). The F_2 ratio will be the same as (a) also. When you have genes on the autosomes (not X-linked), independent assortment, complete dominance, and no gene interaction (see later) in a cross involving double heterozygotes, the offspring ratio will be in the ratio 9:3:3:1.

(c)

> P_1:
>
>   *EEVV X EEvv*
>
> F_1: *EEVv* (grey, long)
>
> F_2: Notice that all the offspring will have grey bodies and you will get a 3:1 ratio of long to vestigial wings. You should see this before you even begin working through the problem. Even though this cross involves two gene pairs, it will give a "monohybrid " type of ratio because one of the gene pairs is homozygous (body color) and **one** gene pair is heterozygous (wing length).
>
> | Phenotypes | Ratio | Genotypes | Ratio |
> |---|---|---|---|
> | grey, long | 3/4 | *EEVV* | 1/4 |
> | | | *EEVv* | 2/4 |
> | grey, vestigial | 1/4 | *EEvv* | 1/4 |

NOTE: After working through this problem, it is important that you try to work similar problems without constructing the time-consuming Punnett squares, especially if each problem asks for phenotypic rather than genotypic ratios.

14. The general formula for determining the number of kinds of gametes produced by an organism is 2^n where n = number of *heterozygous* gene pairs.

    (a) 4: *AB, Ab, aB, ab*

    (b) 2: *AB, aB*

    (c) 8: *ABC, ABc, AbC, Abc, aBC, aBc, abC, abc*

    (d) 2: *ABc, aBc*

    (e) 4: *ABc, Abc, aBc, abc*

    (f) $2^5 = 32$

ABCDE	aBCDE
ABCDe	aBCDe
ABCdE	aBCdE
ABCde	aBCde
ABcDE	aBcDE
ABcDe	aBcDe
ABcdE	aBcdE
ABcde	aBcde
AbCDE	abCDE
AbCDe	abCDe
AbCdE	abCdE
AbCde	abCde
AbcDE	abcDE
AbcDe	abcDe
AbcdE	abcdE
Abcde	abcde

Notice that there is a pattern that can be used to write these gametes so that fewer errors will occur.

15.

(a) When examining this cross

    AaBbCc X AaBBCC

expect there to be eight different kinds of gametes from one parent (*AaBbCc*), and two different kinds from the other (*AaBBCC*). Therefore there should be sixteen kinds (genotypes) of offpsring (8 X 2).

Gametes:	Gametes:
ABC	*ABC*
ABc	*aBC*
AbC	
Abc	
aBC	
aBc	
abC	
abc	

Offspring:

Genotypes	Ratio	Phenotypes
AABBCC	(1/16)	
AABBCc	(1/16)	
AABbCC	(1/16)	
AABbCc	(1/16)	
AaBBCC	(2/16)	A_B_C_ = 12/16
AaBBCc	(2/16)	
AaBbCC	(2/16)	
AaBbCc	(2/16)	
aaBBCC	(1/16)	
aaBBCc	(1/16)	aaB_C_ = 4/16
aaBbCC	(1/16)	
aaBbCc	(1/16)	

(b) There will be four kinds of gametes for the first parent (AaBBCc) and two kinds of gametes for the second parent.

Gametes: Gametes:

ABC
ABc
aBC
aBc

aBC
aBc

Offspring:

Genotypes	Ratio	Phenotypes	
AaBBCC	1/8	A_BBC_	= 3/8
AaBBCc	2/8		
AaBBcc	1/8	A_BBcc	= 1/8
aaBBCC	1/8	aaBBC_	= 3/8
aaBBCc	2/8		
aaBBcc	1/8	aaBBcc	= 1/8

(c) There will be eight (2^n) different kinds of gametes from each of the parents, therefore a 64-box Punnett square. Doing this problem by the forked-line method helps considerably.

```
                              1/4 CC = 1/64 AABBCC
                 1/4 BB ───── 2/4 Cc = 2/64 AABBCc
                              1/4 cc
                              1/4 CC          etc.
1/4 AA   2/4 Bb ───── 2/4 Cc
                              1/4 cc
                              1/4 CC
                 1/4 bb ───── 2/4 Cc
                              1/4 cc
```

		1/4 CC
	1/4 BB	2/4 Cc
		1/4 cc
		1/4 CC
2/4 Aa	2/4 Bb	2/4 Cc
		1/4 cc
		1/4 CC
	1/4 bb	2/4 Cc
		1/4 cc
		1/4 CC
	1/4 BB	2/4 Cc
		1/4 cc
		1/4 CC
1/4 aa	2/4 Bb	2/4 Cc
		1/4 cc
		1/4 CC
	1/4 bb	2/4 Cc
		1/4 cc

Simply multiply through each component to arrive at the final genotypic frequencies.

For the phenotypic frequencies, set up the problem in the following manner.

$$
\begin{array}{ccc}
 & 3/4\ C\_ & = 27/64\ A\_B\_C\_ \\
3/4\ B\_ & 1/4\ cc & = 9/64\ A\_B\_cc
\end{array}
$$

3/4 A_ — 1/4 bb $\diagdown$ 3/4 C_   etc.
1/4 cc

1/4 aa — 3/4 B_ — 3/4 C_
$\diagdown$ 1/4 cc

1/4 bb — 3/4 C_
1/4 cc

16. In reading this question, notice that there are two characteristics being considered; seed color (yellow, green) and seed shape (round, wrinkled). At this point you should be able to do this problem without writing down each of the steps. The F_1 can be considered to be a double heterozygote (with round and yellow being dominant). See the cross this way:

Symbols:

Seed shape   *Seed color*

W = round G = yellow
w = wrinkled g = green

P_1:

$WWgg \quad X \quad wwGG$

F_1: $WwGg$ cross to $wwgg$

(which is a typical test cross)

The offspring will occur in a typical 1:1:1:1 as

1/4 $WwGg$ (round, yellow)

1/4 $Wwgg$ (round, green)

1/4 $wwGg$ (wrinkled, yellow)

1/4 $wwgg$ (wrinkled, green)

Again, at this point it would be very helpful if you could do such simple problems by inspection.

17. Since these are F_2 results from monohybrid crosses, a 3:1 ratio is expected for each. Referring to the *Essentials* text one can set up the analysis easily.

(a)

Expected ratio	Observed (o)	Expected (e)
3/4	882	885.75
1/4	299	295.25

Expected values are derived by multiplying the expected ratio by the total number of organisms.

$$\chi^2 = \Sigma \ \frac{(o - e)^2}{e} \ = 0.064$$

34

In looking in the χ^2 table in the *Essentials* text, with 1 degree of freedom (because there were two classes, therefore n-1 or 1 degree of freedom), we find a probability (*p*) value between 0.9 and 0.5.

We would therefore say that there is a "good fit" between the observed and expected values. Notice that as the deviations between the observed and expected values increase, the value of χ^2 increases. So, the higher the χ^2 value, the more likely the null hypothesis will be rejected.

(b)

Expected ratio	Observed (o)	Expected (e)
3/4	705	696.75
1/4	224	232.25

$$\chi^2 = 0.39$$

The *p*value in the table for 1 degree of freedom is still between 0.9 and 0.5, however because the χ^2 value is larger in (b) we should say that the deviations from expectation are greater.

18. One must think of this problem as a dihybrid F_2 situation with the following expectations:

Expected ratio	Observed (o)	Expected (e)
9/16	315	312.75
3/16	108	104.25
3/16	101	104.25
1/16	32	34.75

$$\chi^2 = 0.47$$

Looking at the table in *Essentials* one can see that this χ^2 value is associated with a probability greater than 0.90 for 3 degrees of freedom (because there are now four classes in the χ^2 test). The observed and expected values do not deviate significantly.

To deal with parts **(b)** and **(c)** it is easier to see the observed values for the monohybrid ratios if the phenotypes are listed:

smooth, yellow	315
smooth, green	108
wrinkled, yellow	101
wrinkled, green	32

For the smooth: wrinkled *monohybrid component*, the smooth types total 423 (315 + 108), while the wrinkled types total 133 (101 + 32).

Expected ratio	Observed (o)	Expected (e)
3/4	423	417
1/4	133	139

The χ^2 value is 0.35 and in examining the table in *Essentials* for 1 degree of freedom, the *p* value is greater than 0.50 and less than 0.90. We fail to reject the null hypothesis and are confident that the observed values do not differ significantly from the expected values.

(c) For the yellow:green portion of the problem, see that there are 416 yellow plants (315 + 101) and 140 (108 + 32) green plants.

Expected ratio	Observed (o)	Expected (e)
3/4	416	417
1/4	140	139

The χ^2 value is 0.01 and in examining the table in *Essentials* for 1 degree of freedom, the P value is greater than 0.90. We fail to reject the null hypothesis and are confident that the observed values do not differ significantly from the expected values.

19. It would be best to set up two tables based on the two hypotheses:

Expected ratio	Observed (o)	Expected (e)
3/4	250	300
1/4	150	100

Expected ratio	Observed (o)	Expected (e)
1/2	250	200
1/2	150	200

For the test of a 3:1 ratio, the χ^2 value is 33.3 with an associated P value of less than 0.01 for 1 degree of freedom.

For the test of a 1:1 ratio, the χ^2 value is 25.0 again with an associated P value of less than 0.01 for 1 degree of freedom. Based on these probability values, both null hypotheses should be rejected.

20. Use of the $p = 0.10$ as the "critical" value for rejecting or failing to reject the null hypothesis instead of P = 0.05 would allow more null hypotheses to be rejected. Notice in the *Essentials* text that as the χ^2 values increase, there is a higher likelihood that the null hypothesis will be rejected because the higher values are more likely to be associated with a p value which is less than 0.05.

As the critical p value is increased, it takes a smaller χ^2 value to cause rejection of the null hypothesis. It would take less difference between the expected and observed values to reject the null hypothesis, therefore the stringency of failing to reject the null hypothesis is increased.

21. Apply the product rule which states that when two or more events occur independently but simultaneously, their combined probability is equal to the product of their individual probabilities.

The probability of getting *AA* from

Aa X AA is 1/2

The probability of getting *Bb* from

Bb X Bb is 1/2

The probability of getting *Cc* from

CC X Cc is 1/2

The overall probability then is

1/2 X 1/2 X 1/2 = 1/8

22. While there are many different inheritance patterns which will be described later in the *Essentials* text (codominance, incomplete dominance, sex-linked inheritance, etc.), the range of solutions to this question is limited to the concepts developed in the first three chapters, namely dominance or recessiveness.

If a gene is dominant, it will not skip generations nor will it be passed to offspring unless the parents possess the gene. On the other hand, genes which are recessive can skip generations and exist in a carrier state in parents. For example, notice that II-4 and II-5 produce a female child (III-4) with the affected phenotype. On these criteria alone, the gene must be viewed as being recessive. Note: if a gene is recessive and X-linked (to be discussed later) the pattern will often be from affected male to carrier female to affected male.

To provide genotypes for each individual, consider that if the box or circle is shaded, the *aa* genotype is to be assigned. If offspring are affected (shaded) a recessive gene must have come from both parents.

I-1 (*Aa*), I-2 (*aa*), I-3 (*Aa*), I-4(*Aa*)

II-1 (*aa*), II-2 (*Aa*), II-3 (*aa*), II-4 (*Aa*), II-5 (*Aa*), II-6 (*aa*), II-7 (*AA or Aa*), II-8 (*AA or Aa*)

III-1 (*AA or Aa*), III-2 (*AA or Aa*), III-3 (*AA or Aa*), III-4 (*aa*), III-5 (probably *AA*), III-6 (*aa*)

IV-1 through IV-7 all *Aa*.

23. *Unit Factors in Pairs*: It is important to see that each time a phenotype (normal or abnormal) is being stated, genotypes are symbolized as pairs of genes; *AA, Aa* or *aa*. Review F3.2 to understand the need to assign appropriate symbols to genes.

Dominance and Recessiveness: Because the gene for non-shaded is completely dominant over the gene for shaded (say *a* is fully recessive), it was necessary to consider, at first, whether non-shaded individuals in the problem were homozygous normal (*AA*) or heterozygous (*Aa*). By looking at the frequency of expression of the recessive gene in the offspring (in *aa* individuals), one can often determine an *Aa* type from an *AA* type.

Segregation: During gamete formation, when homologous chromosomes move to opposite poles, paired elements (genes) separate from each other.

24. Appling the same logic as in a previous pedigree question, the gene is inherited as an autosomal recessive. Notice that two normal individuals in II-3 and II-4 have produced a daughter (III-2) with myopia.

I-1 (*aa*), I-2 (*AA or Aa*), I-3 (*Aa*), I-4 (*Aa*)

II-1 (*Aa*), II-2 (*Aa*), II-3 (*Aa*), II-4(*Aa*), II-5 (*aa*), II-6 (*AA or Aa*), II-7 (*AA or Aa*)

III-1 (*AA or Aa*), III-2 (*aa*), III-3 (*AA or Aa*)

25. (a) There are two possibilities. Either the trait is dominant, in which case I-1 is heterozygous as are II-2 and II-3, or the trait is recessive and I-1 is homozygous and I-2 is heterozygous. Under the condition of recessiveness, both II-1 and II-4 would be heterozygous, II-2 and II-3 homozygous.

(b) Recessive: Parents *Aa, Aa*

(c) Recessive: Parents *Aa, Aa*

(d) Recessive: Parents *AA* (probably), *aa* Second pedigree: Recessive or dominant, not sex-linked, if recessive, parents *Aa, aa*

(e) See initial explanation in this problem. It is essentially the same as the first pedigree.

26. (a) First consider that each parent is homozygous (true-breeding in the question) and since in the F_1 only round, axial, violet, and full phenotypes were expressed, they must each be dominant.

(b) Round, axial, violet and full would be the most frequent phenotypes:

3/4 X 3/4 X 3/4 X 3/4

(c) Wrinkled, terminal, white, and constricted would be the least frequent phenotypes:

1/4 X 1/4 X 1/4 X 1/4

(d) 3/4 X 1/4 X 3/4 X 1/4

(e) There would be 16 different phenotypes in the test cross offspring just as there are 16 different phenotypes in the F_2 generation.

27. (a) The first task is to draw out an accurate pedigree (one of several possibilities):

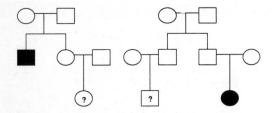

(b) The probability that the female (whose maternal uncle had TSD) is heterozygous is 1/3 because she is not TSD and her mother had a 2/3 chance of being heterozygous. Given that her mother is heterozygous, she has a 1/2 chance of passing the TSD gene to her daughter (2/3 X 1/2 = 1/3). The male (whose paternal first cousin had TSD) has a 1/4 chance of being heterozygous, assuming that either (but not both, because the gene is said to be rare) his grandmother or grandfather was heterozygous. Therefore the probability that both the male and female are heterozygous is:

$$1/3 \text{ X } 1/4 = 1/12$$

(c) The probability that neither is heterozygous is:

$$2/3 \text{ X } 3/4 = 6/12$$

(d) The probability that one is heterozygous is:

$$(1/3 \text{ X } 3/4) + (2/3 \text{ X } 1/4) = 5/12$$

28.

(a) Notice in cross #1 that the ratio of straight wings to curled wings is 3:1 and the ratio of short bristles to long bristles is also 3:1. This would indicate that straight is dominant to curled and short is dominant to long. Possible symbols would be (using standard *Drosophila* symbolism):

straight wings = w^+ curled wings = w

short bristles = b^+ long bristles = b

(b)

Cross #1: w^+/w ; b^+/b X w^+/w ; b^+/b

Cross #2: w^+/w ; b/b X w^+/w ; b/b

Cross #3: w/w ; b/b X w^+/w ; b^+/b

Cross #4: w^+/w^+ ; b^+/b X w^+/w^+ ; b^+/b
          (one parent could be w^+/w)

Cross #5: w/w ; b^+/b X w^+/w ; b^+/b

Chapter 4: Modification of Mendelian Ratios

Concept Areas

Corresponding Problems

Incomplete Dominance, Codominance   1, 2, 4, 5, 6, 17, 25
Epistasis   7, 9, 20
Novel Phenotypes   8, 18, 19, 22
Multiple Alleles   3, 21
Complementation   24
Sex Linkage   10, 11, 12, 13, 14, 15, 16, 23

Vocabulary and Critical Issues

Structures and Substances

Allele (wild type, mutant)

   hexosaminidase

   complementation group

X chromosome

Y chromosome

Processes/Methods

Incomplete (partial) dominance

   pink flowers

   1:2:1 phenotypic ratio

Codominance

   $L^M L^N$ alleles (MN blood groups)

   3:6:3:1:2:1

Multiple alleles

   $I^A\ I^B\ I^O$ (ABO blood groups)

antigen-antibody reaction

   isoagglutinogen

   H substance

   Bombay phenotype

white eye in *Drosophila*

Lethal alleles

   recessive

   dominant

     yellow coat color in mice

     Huntington disease

Gene interaction: discontinuous variation

   epistasis

   hypostatic

     coat color in mammals

     Bombay phenotype

      9:3:4

dominant

    fruit color in squash

    12:3:1

other

    white flowers in peas

    9:7

    novel phenotypes

    fruit shape in *Cucurbita*

Gene interaction: continuous variation

Complementation analysis

    cis-trans test

Sex linkage (X-linkage)

    hemizygous

    crisscross pattern

Pedigree analysis

Sex-limited inheritance

Sex-influenced inheritance

Phenotypic expression

    Expressivity

    Penetrance

Genetic anticipation

Genomic (parental) imprinting

Concepts

Gene interaction (F4.1)

Neo-Mendelian genetics

Allele (F4.2)

    wild type

    mutation

        loss of wild type function

        reduced or increased function

Symbolism (F4.2)

    recessive trait (D, d; e,e^+)

    dominant trait (Wr, Wr^+)

    "+" as a superscript

    + as a symbol for wild type ($+/e$)

    no dominance (R^1, R^2)

Modified ratios (T4.1)

    3:1

      1:2:1

    9:3:3:1

      3:6:3:1:2:1

      9:3:4

      12:3:1

      9:7

      1:4:6:4:1

Continuous/discontinuous variation

Complementation

Other patterns of inheritance

T4.1. Examples of typical monohybrid and dihybrid ratios and several modifications.

Basic Ratio	Modification	Explanation
3:1	1:2:1	Incomplete dominance
		Codominance
9:3:3:1	9:3:4	Epistasis
	12:3:1	Epistasis
	9:7	Epistasis
	3:6:3:1:2:1	Dominance + incomplete dominance or codominance

F4.1. Illustration of gene interaction where products from more than one gene pair influence one characteristic or phenotypic trait.

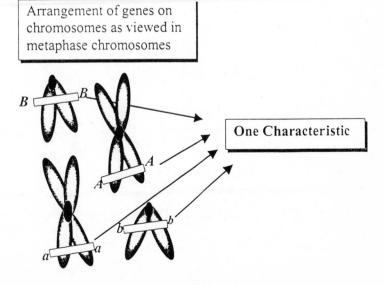

Arrangement of genes on chromosomes as viewed in metaphase chromosomes

One Characteristic

F4.2. Illustration of the symbolism associated with the wild type activity of a gene and several possible outcomes of the mutant state (*m/m*).

First, too much product (B) is made in the mutant state.

Second, too little product is made.

Third, no product is made.

The presence of the wild type allele (+) allows for the normal conversion of substrate A to product B.

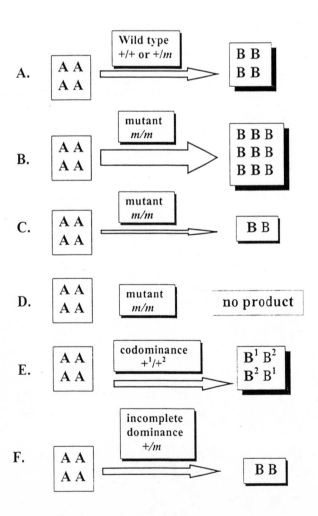

Solutions to Problems and Discussion Questions

1. In the first sentence of this problem, notice that there is one characteristic (coat color) and three phenotypes mentioned; red, white, or roan. The fact that roan is intermediate between red and white suggests that this may be a case of codominance, with roan being the intermediate. If that is the case then we should suspect a 1:2:1 phenotypic ratio in crosses of "roan to roan."

Looking at the data given, notice that a cross of the "extremes" (red X white) gives roan, suggesting its heterozygous nature and the homozygous nature of the parents. Seeing the 1:2:1 ratio in the offspring of

roan X roan

confirms the hypothesis of codominance as the mode of inheritance.

Symbolism:

```
AA = red

aa = white

Aa = roan
```

Crosses: It is important at this point that you not be fully dependent on writing out complete Punnett squares for each cross. Begin working these simple problems in your head.

```
AA    X    AA    -->    AA

aa    X    aa    -->    aa

AA    X    aa    -->    Aa

Aa    X    Aa    -->    1/4 AA;
                        2/4 Aa; 1/4 aa
```

2. *Incomplete dominance* can be viewed more as a quantitative phenomenon where the heterozygote is intermediate (approximately) between the limits set by the homozygotes. Pink is intermediate between red and white.

Codominance can be viewed in a more qualitative manner where both of the alleles in the heterozygote are expressed. For example in the AB blood group, both the I^A and I^B genes are expressed . There is no intermediate class which is part I^A and I^B.

3. In this problem remember that individuals with blood type B can have the genotype $I^B I^B$ or $I^B I^o$ and those with blood type A can have the genotypes $I^A I^A$ or $I^A I^o$.

Male Parent: must be $I^B I^o$ because the mother is $I^o I^o$ and one inherits one homologue (therefore one allele) from each parent.

Female Parent: must be $I^A I^o$ because the father is $I^B I^o$ and one inherits one homologue (therefore one allele) from each parent. The father cannot be $I^B I^B$ and have a daughter of blood type A.

Offspring:

$I^A I^o$ X $I^B I^o$

	I^B	I^o
I^A	$I^A I^B$(AB)	$I^A I^o$(A)
I^o	$I^B I^o$ (B)	$I^o I^o$(O)

The ratio would be 1(A):1(B):1(AB):1(O).

4. Notice that there is one typical (coat color) and one atypical (lethality) characteristic mentioned. Often under this condition of two characteristics, we must decide if the problem involves one or more than one gene pair. Because the genotypes are given here it is obvious that lethality is associated with expression of the coat color alleles and therefore one gene pair is involved. This is a monohybrid condition.

> Pp X Pp —>
>
> $1/4$ PP (**lethal**)
>
> $2/4$ Pp (platinum)
>
> $1/4$ pp (silver)

Therefore the ratio of surviving foxes is $2/3$ platinum, $1/3$ silver. The P allele behaves as a recessive in terms of lethality (seen only in the homozygote) but as a dominant in terms of coat color (seen in the homozygote).

5. Three independently assorting characteristics are being dealt with: flower color (incomplete dominance), flower shape (dominant/recessive), and plant height (dominant/recessive). Establish appropriate gene symbols:

> Flower color:
>
> RR = red ; Rr = pink; rr = white
>
> Flower shape:
>
> P = personate; p = peloric
>
> Plant height:
>
> D = tall; d = dwarf

(a)

> $RRPPDD$ X $rrppdd$ —>
>
> $RrPpDd$ (pink, personate, tall)

(b) Use *components* of the forked line method as follows:

> $2/4$ pink X $3/4$ personate X $3/4$ tall
>
> = 18/64

6. There are two characteristics, flower color and flower shape. Because pink results from a cross of red and white, one would conclude that flower color is "monohybrid" with incomplete dominance.

In addition, because personate is seen in the F_1 when personate and peloric are crossed, personate must be dominant to peloric. Results from crosses (c) and (d) verify these conclusions. The appropriate symbols would be as follows:

> Flower color:
>
> RR = red; Rr = pink; rr = white
>
> Flower shape:
>
> P = personate; p = peloric

(a)

> $RRpp$ X $rrPP$ ---> $RrPp$

(b)

> $RRPP$ X $rrpp$ ---> $RrPp$

(c)

RrPp   X   RRpp   ---> RRPp
                       RRpp
                       RrPp
                       Rrpp

(d)

RrPp   X   rrpp   ---> rrPp
                       rrpp
                       RrPp
                       Rrpp

In the cross of the F₁ of (a) to the F₁ of (b), both of which are double heterozygotes, one would expect the following:

RrPp   X   RrPp

1/4 red
  3/4 personate —> 3/16 red, personate
  1/4 peloric   —> 1/16 red, peloric

2/4 pink
  3/4 personate —> 6/16 pink, personate
  1/4 peloric   —> 2/16 pink, peloric

1/4 white
  3/4 personate —> 3/16 white, personate
  1/4 peloric   —> 1/16 white, peloric

7. Notice that the distribution of observed offspring fits a 9:3:4 ratio quite well. This suggests that two independently assorting gene pairs with epistasis are involved. Assign gene symbols in the usual manner:

A = pigment; a = pigmentless (colorless)

B = purple; b = red

AaBb   X   AaBb

produces

9   A_B_   = purple
3   A_bb   = red
3   aaB_   = colorless
1   aabb   = colorless

One may see this occurring in the following manner:

precursor —+-> cyanidin —+-> purple pigment
(colorless) aa (red) bb

8. This is a case of gene interaction (novel phenotypes) where the yellow and black types (double mutants) interact to give the cream phenotype and epistasis where the cc genotype produces albino.

(a)

AaBbCc —> gray (C allows pigment)

(b)

> A_B_Cc —>
>
> gray (*C* allows pigment)

(c) Use the forked line method for this portion:

```
                          1/2 Cc —> 9/32 gray
               3/4 B_     1/2 cc —> 9/32 albino

3/4 A_
                          1/2 Cc —> 3/32 yellow
               1/4 bb     1/2 cc —> 3/32 albino

                          1/2 Cc —> 3/32 black
               3/4 B_     1/2 cc —> 3/32 albino

1/4 aa     1/4 bb     1/2 Cc —> 1/32 cream
                      1/2 cc —> 1/32 albino
```

Combining the phenotypes gives (always count the proportions to see that they add up to 1.0):

   16/32 albino

   9/32 gray

   3/32 yellow

   3/32 black

   1/32 cream

9. Treat each of the crosses as a series of monohybrid crosses, remembering that albino is epistatic to color and black and yellow interact to give cream.

(a) Since this is a 9:3:3:1 ratio with no albino phenotypes, the parents must each have been double heterozygotes and incapable of producing the *cc* genotype.

> Genotypes:
>
>   *AaBbCC* X *AaBbCC*
>
>   or
>
>   *AaBbCC* X *AaBbCc*
>
> Phenotypes: gray X gray

(b) Since there are no black offspring, there are no combinations in the parents which can produce *aa*. The 4/16 proportion indicates that the *C* locus is heterozygous in both parents. If the parents are as follows

> *AABbCc* X *AaBbCc*
>
> or
>
> *AABbCc* X *AABbCc*

then the results would follow the pattern given.

Phenotypes: gray X gray

(c) Notice that 16/64 or 1/4 of the offspring are albino, therefore the parents are both heterozygous at the *C* locus. Second, notice that without considering the *C* locus, there is a 27:9:9:3 ratio which reduces to a 9:3:3:1 ratio. Given this information, the genotypes must be

> *AaBbCc* X *AaBbCc.*
>
> Phenotypes: gray X gray

10. In order to solve this problem one must first see the possible genotypes of the parents and the grandfathers. Since the gene is X-linked, the cross will be symbolized with the X chromosomes.

RG = normal vision; rg = color-blind

    Mother's father: X^{rg}/Y

    Father's father: X^{rg}/Y

    Mother: $X^{RG} X^{rg}$

    Father: X^{RG}/Y

Notice that the mother must be heterozygous for the rg allele (being normal-visioned and having inherited an X^{rg} from her father) and the father, because he has normal vision, must be X^{RG}. The fact that the father's father is color-blind does not mean that the father will be color-blind. On the contrary, the father will inherit his X chromosome from his mother.

$X^{RG} X^{rg}$ X X^{RG}/Y —>

$X^{RG} X^{RG}$ = 1/4 daughter normal

$X^{RG} X^{rg}$ = 1/4 daughter normal

X^{RG}/Y = 1/4   son normal

X^{rg}/Y = 1/4   son color-blind

Looking at the distribution of offspring:

(a) 1/4

(b) 1/2

(c) 1/4

(d) zero

11. The mating is

$X^{RG}X^{rg}; I^A I^O$ X $X^{RG}Y; I^A I^O$

Based on the son who is colorblind and blood type O, the mother must have been heterozygous for the RG locus and both parents must have had one copy of the I^O gene. The probability of having a female child is 1/2, that she has normal vision is 1.0 (because the father's X is normal) and 1/4 type O blood. The final product of the independent probabilities is

$$1/2 \ X \ 1 \ X \ 1/4 \ = \ 1/8$$

12. In seeing that the distribution of phenotypes in the F_1 is different when comparing males and females, it would be tempting to suggest that the gene is X-linked. However, given that the reciprocal cross gives identical results suggests that the gene is autosomal. Seeing the different distribution between males and females, one might consider sex-influenced inheritance as a model and have males more likely to express mahogany and females more likely to express red. This situation is similar to pattern baldness in humans. Consider two alleles which are autosomal and let

---

RR = red, Rr = red in females

Rr = mahogany in males

rr = mahogany

P_1:

female: RR (red)   X   male: rr (mahogany)

F_1:

    Rr = females red; males mahogany

    1/2 females (red)

    1/2 males (mahogany)

F_2:

    1/4 RR: 2/4 Rr: 1/4 rr

Because half of the offspring are males and half are females, one could, for clarity, rewrite the F_2 as:

	1/2 females	1/2 males
1/4 RR	1/8 red	1/8 red
2/4 Rr	2/8 red	2/8 mahogany
1/4 rr	1/8 mahogany	1/8 mahogany

13. This problem incorporates X-linked inheritance with mosaicism caused by X chromosome inactivation. The following symbolism is appropriate:

B = black coat color; b = yellow coat color

Female tortoise-shell = $X^B X^b$ (mosaic)
Male black   = $X^B Y$

$X^B X^b$ X $X^B Y$ —>

  1/4 $X^B X^B$ = female black

  1/4 $X^B X^b$ = female tortoise-shell

  1/4 $X^B Y$ = male black

  1/4 $X^b Y$ = male yellow

Normally there is no way for a tortoise-shell male to be produced, however with nondisjunction of the X chromosome in the female parent producing a gamete containing the two X chromosomes, the coat color genes could be in the heterozygous state and mosaicism may result. The nondisjunctional event must occur in meiosis I. If such a female gamete is fertilized by a Y-bearing sperm, then an XXY tortoise-shell male could result.

14.

Symbolism:

    Normal wing margins = sd^+

    scalloped = sd

(a)

P1:

    $X^{sd} X^{sd}$ X X^+/Y —>
(assume homozygous)

    F_1:

        1/2 $X^+ X^{sd}$ (female, normal)

        1/2 X^{sd}/Y (male, scalloped)

    F_2:

        1/4 $X^+ X^{sd}$ (female, normal)

        1/4 $X^{sd} X^{sd}$ (female, scalloped)

        1/4 X^+/Y (male, normal)

        1/4 X^{sd}/Y (male, scalloped)

(b)

P1:

X^+/X^+ X X^{sd}/Y —>

F$_1$:

1/2 X^+X^{sd} (female, normal)

1/2 X^+/Y (male, normal)

F$_2$:

1/4 X^+X^+ (female, normal)

1/4 X^+X^{sd} (female, normal)

1/4 X^+/Y (male, normal)

1/4 X^{sd}/Y (male, scalloped)

If the *scalloped* gene were not X-linked, then all of the F$_1$ offspring would be wild (phenotypically) and a 3:1 ratio of normal to scalloped would occur in the F$_2$.

15. Assuming that the parents are homozygous, the crosses would be as follows. Notice that the X symbol may remain to remind us that the *sd* gene is on the X chromosome. It is extremely important that one account for both the mutant genes and each of their wild type alleles.

P$_1$:

$X^{sd}X^{sd}$; e^+/e^+ X X^+/Y; e/e —>

F$_1$:

1/2 X^+X^{sd}; e^+/e (female, normal)

1/2 X^{sd}/Y; e^+/e (male, scalloped)

F$_2$:

	X^+e^+	X^+e	$X^{sd}e^+$	$X^{sd}e$
$X^{sd}e^+$				
$X^{sd}e$				
Ye^+				
Ye				

Phenotypes:

3/16 normal females

3/16 normal males

1/16 ebony females

1/16 ebony males

3/16 scalloped females

3/16 scalloped males

1/16 scalloped, ebony females

1/16 scalloped, ebony males

Forked-line method:

P$_1$:

$X^{sd}X^{sd}$; e^+/e^+ X X^+/Y; e/e —>

F$_1$:

1/2 X^+X^{sd}; e^+/e (female, normal)

1/2 X^{sd}/Y; e^+/e (male, scalloped)

F$_2$:

Wings	Color	
1/4 females, normal	3/4 normal	3/16
	1/4 ebony	1/16
1/4 females, scalloped	3/4 normal	3/16
	1/4 ebony	1/16
1/4 males, normal	3/4 normal	3/16
	1/4 ebony	1/16
1/4 males, scalloped	3/4 normal	3/16
	1/4 ebony	1/16

16. It is extremely important that one account for both the mutant genes and each of their wild type alleles.

(a)

P$_1$: X^vX^v; $+/+$ X X^+/Y; b^r/b^r —>

F$_1$:

1/2 X^+X^v; $+/b^r$ (female, normal)

1/2 X^v/Y; $+/b^r$ (male, vermilion)

F$_2$:

Eye color(X)   Eye color(autosomal)

1/4 females, normal	3/4 normal	3/16	
	1/4 brown	1/16	
1/4 females, vermilion	3/4 normal	3/16	
	1/4 brown	1/16	
1/4 males, normal	3/4 normal	3/16	
	1/4 brown	1/16	
1/4 males, vermilion	3/4 normal	3/16	
	1/4 brown	1/16	

3/16   = females, normal

1/16   = females, brown eyes

3/16   = females, vermilion eyes

1/16   = females, white eyes

3/16   = males, normal

1/16   = males, brown eyes

3/16   = males, vermilion eyes

1/16   = males, white eyes

(b)

P$_1$: X^+X^+; b^r/b^r X X^v/Y; $+/+$ —>

F$_1$:

1/2 X^+X^v; $+/b^r$ (female, normal)

1/2 X^+/Y; $+/b^r$ (male, normal)

F$_2$:   Eye color(X)   Eye color(autosomal)

2/4 females, normal	3/4 normal		
	1/4 brown		
1/4 males, normal	3/4 normal		
	1/4 brown		
1/4 males, vermilion	3/4 normal		
	1/4 brown		

6/16   = females, normal

2/16   = females, brown eyes

3/16   = males, normal

1/16   = males, brown eyes

3/16   = males, vermilion eyes

1/16   = males, white eyes

(c)

P$_1$:

X^vX^v; b^r/b^r X X^+/Y; +/+ —>

F$_1$:

1/2 X^+X^v; +/b^r (female, normal)
1/2 X^v/Y; +/b^r (male, vermilion)

F$_2$:   Eye color(X)   Eye color(autosomal)

1/4   females,   3/4 normal
      normal   1/4 brown

1/4   females,   3/4 normal
      vermilion 1/4 brown

1/4   males,   3/4 normal
      normal   1/4 brown

1/4   males,   3/4 normal
      vermilion 1/4 brown

3/16   = females, normal

1/16   = females, brown eyes

3/16   = females, vermilion eyes

1/16   = females, white eyes

3/16   = males, normal

1/16   = males, brown eyes

3/16   = males, vermilion eyes

1/16   = males, white eyes

17. Consider the solution in the following general manner. From cross number one, one should think about there being two gene loci which interact to give the phenotypes noted. Notice that two true-breeding sandy lines give red. This would happen if the following situation occurred:

s^1/s^1;S^2/S^2 or S^1/S^1;s^2/s^2 homozygous strains each the sandy phenotype; also, as long as there is one upper case S, the sandy phenotype will prevail.

When crossed with each other they give the double heterozygotes:

S^1/s^1;s^2/S^2 which gives the red phenotype because both S^1 and S^2 are present.

The white phenoytpe occurs when neither S^1 nor S^2 are present: s^1/s^1; s^2/s^2

Because crosses #1 and #4 are among double heterozygotes, independent assortment is occurring, and there are two ways to get the sandy phenotype, both F$_2$ results would be the following:

9 (red): 6(sandy): 1(white)

18. (a) Because the denominator in the ratios is 64 one would begin to consider that there are three independently assorting gene pairs. Because there are only two characteristics (eye color and croaking) however, one might consider two gene pairs interacting for one trait.

(b) Notice that there is a 48:16 (or 3:1) ratio of rib-it to knee-deep and a 36:16:12 (9:3:4) ratio of blue to green to purple eye color. Because of these relationships one would conclude that croaking is due to one gene pair while eye color is due to two gene pairs.

(c) Croaking: $R\_$ = rib-it; rr = knee-deep

$A\_B\_$ = blue eyed
A_bb = purple
$aaB\_$ and $aabb$ = green

(d) Parents: *AABBrr* X *AAbbRR*

F₁: *AABbRr*

F₂: 9/16 *AAB_R_* = blue-eyed, utterer

3/16 *AAB_rr* = blue-eyed, mutterer

3/16 *AAbbR_* = purple-eyed, utterer

1/16 *AAbbrr* = purple-eyed, mutterer

19. In doing these type of problems, take each characteristic individually, then build the complete genotypes. *AabbRr*

20. The second sentence in the problem indicates that solid white is dominant to solid black. The 12:3:1 ratio indicates the a modification of a dihybrid ratio exists and that some form of epistasis is occurring. In the first cross let the symbols be as follows:

> *WWAA* X *wwaa*
> (white) (black)
>
> F₁: *WwAa* X *WwAa* (all solid white)
>
> F₂: 9/16 *W_A_* = solid white
> 3/16 *W_aa* = solid white
> 3/16 *wwA_* = spotted
> 1/16 *wwaa* = solid black

So, *W* is epistatic to *A*. It would be possible to isolate a true-breeding strain of black and white spotted cattle; *wwAA*..

21. It is important to see that this problem involves multiple alleles, meaning that monohybrid type ratios are expected, and that there is an order of dominance which will allow certain alleles to be "hidden" in various heterozygotes. As with most genetics problems, one must look at the phenotypes of the offspring to assess the genotypes of the parents.

(a)

> Parents: sepia X cream

Because both guinea pigs had albino parents, both are heterozygous for the c^a allele.

> Cross: $c^k c^a$ X $c^d c^a$ —>
>
> 2/4 sepia; 1/4 cream; 1/4 albino

(b)

> Parents: sepia X cream

Because the sepia parent had an albino parent it must be $c^k c^a$. Because the cream guinea pig had two sepia parents

$$(c^k c^d \ X \quad c^k c^d \ \text{or} \ c^k c^d \ X \quad c^k c^a),$$

the cream parent could be $c^d c^d$ or $c^d c^a$.

> Crosses:
>
> $c^k c^a$ X $c^d c^d$ —>
>
> 1/2 sepia; 1/2 cream*
>
> *(if parents are assumed to be homozygous)
>
> or
>
> $c^k c^a$ X $c^d c^a$ —>
>
> 1/2 sepia; 1/4 cream; 1/4 albino

(c)

> Parents: sepia X cream

Because the sepia guinea pig had two full color parents which could be

$$Cc^k, \quad Cc^d, \ \text{or} \ Cc^a$$

(not *CC* because sepia could not be produced), its genotype could be

$$c^k c^k, \quad c^k c^d, \ \text{or} \ c^k c^a.$$

Because the cream guinea pig had two sepia parents

$$(c^k c^d \ X \ \ c^k c^d \ \text{or} \ \ c^k c^d \ X \ \ c^k c^a),$$

the cream parent could be $c^d c^d$ or $c^d c^a$.

Crosses:

$c^k c^k \ X \ c^d c^d \longrightarrow$ all sepia

$c^k c^k \ X \ c^d c^a \longrightarrow$ all sepia

$c^k c^d \ X \ c^d c^d \longrightarrow$ 1/2 sepia; 1/2 cream

$c^k c^d \ X \ c^d c^a \longrightarrow$ 1/2 sepia; 1/2 cream

$c^k c^a \ X \ c^d c^d \longrightarrow$ 1/2 sepia; 1/2 cream

$c^k c^a \ X \ c^d c^a \longrightarrow$

   1/2 sepia; 1/4 cream; 1/4 albino

(d)

Parents: sepia X cream

Because the sepia parent had two full color parents

$$(Cc^k \ X \ Cc^k, Cc^d, Cc^a),$$

it could be be $c^k c^k$, $c^k c^d$, $c^k c^a$. The cream parent had two full color parents which could be Cc^d or Cc^a; therefore it could be $c^d c^d$ or $c^d c^a$.

   Crosses: for example

$c^k c^a \ X \ c^d c^d \longrightarrow$ 1/2 sepia; 1/2 cream

$c^k c^a \ X \ c^d c^a \longrightarrow$

   1/2 sepia; 1/4 cream; 1/4 albino

Complete the crosses with the other sepia parents and collect the offspring phenotypes

---

22. (a)

(i) $BbYy$ = green parents

(ii, iii)

   $B\_Y\_$ = green progeny (9/16)

   B_yy = blue progeny (3/16)

   $bbY\_$ = yellow progeny (3/16)

   $bbyy$ = albino progeny (1/16)

(b) $BByy \ X \ bbYY$ or $BBYY \ X \ bbyy$

23. (a,b) In looking at the pedigrees, one can see that the condition cannot be dominant because it appears in the offspring (II-3 and II-4) and not the parents in the first two cases. The condition is therefore *recessive*. In the second cross, note that the father is not shaded yet the daughter (II-4) is. If the condition is recessive, then it must also be *autosomal*.

(c) II-1 = AA or Aa

   II-6 = AA or Aa

   II-9 = Aa

24. In Cross 1, the offspring are wild type, indicating complementation; thus the genes are non-allelic. For Cross 2, the offspring have the mutant phenotype indicating lack of complementation; thus the genes are allelic. Since $r1$ and $r3$ are allelic, and $r2$ is not allelic to $r1$ (see Cross 1), $r2$ must not be allelic to $r3$. Therefore, in the cross $r2 \ X \ r3$, complementation should occur and wild type eyes should be the result.

25. First, look for familiar ratios which will inform you as to the general mode of inheritance. Notice that the last cross (h) gives a 9:4:3 ratio which is typical of epistasis. From this information one can develop a model to account for the results given.

Symbolism:

A-B- = black

A-bb = golden
aabb = golden

aaB- = brown

The combination of *bb* is epistatic to the *A* locus.

(a) *AAB-* X *aaBB* (other configurations possible but each must give all offspring with *A* and *B* dominant alleles)

(b) *AaB-* X *aaBB* (other configurations are possible but no *bb* types can be produced)

(c) *AABb* X *aaBb*

(d) *AABB* X *aabb*

(e) *AaBb* X *Aabb*

(f) *AaBb* X *aabb*

(g) *aaBb* X *aaBb*

(h) *AaBb* X *AaBb*

Those genotypes which will breed true will be as follows:

black = *AABB*

golden = all genotypes which are *bb*

brown = *aaBB*

Chapter 5: Sex Determination and Sex Chromosomes

Concept Areas	Corresponding Problems
Sex Chromosomes	1, 3, 6, 7, 17
Sex Determination	14, 15, 16, 17
Sexual Differentiation	16
Dosage Compensation	8, 9, 10, 11, 12, 13

Vocabulary and Critical Issues

Structures and Substances

Heteromorphic sex chromosomes

isogamete

zoospore

gametophyte

sporophyte

stamen (tassels)

microgametophyte

pistil

endosperm nuclei

oocyte nucleus

synergids

antipodal nuclei

heterochromosome

Y chromosome

heterogametic sex

homogametic sex

aromatase

Testis determining factor (TDF)

glucose-6-phosphate dehydrogenase deficiency (G-6-PD)

clone

X-inactivation center (XIC)

X-inactive specific transcript (XIST)

Xic, Xist (mouse)

open reading frame (ORF)

transformer gene (*tra*)

Sex-lethal (*Sxl*)

double-sex (*dsx*)

Processes/ Methods

Sexual Differentiation

primary, secondary

unisexual

dioecious

gonochoric

bisexual

monoecious

hermaphroditic

intersex

Chlamydomonas

  isogametes

Zea mays

  double fertilization

C. elegans

XX/XO *Protenor* mode

XX/XY *Lygaeus* mode

ZZ/ZW

Sex determination (humans)

  XX = female, XY = male

    intersexuality

  Klinefelter syndrome 47, XXY

  48, XXXY,

  48, XXYY, etc.

  Turner syndrome 45, X

  mosaics 45X/46XY, 45X/46XX

  47, XXX; 48, XXXX;

  49, XXXXX

  47, XYY

  sexual differentiation

    gonadal primordia

    cortex, medulla

human Y chromosome

    pseudoautosomal regions (PARS)

    NRY

    testis determining factor (TDF)

    sex determining region (SRY)

      XX males

      XY females

      transgenic mice

Sex ratio (humans)

  primary

  secondary

Dosage compensation

  sex chromatin body (Barr body)

  N-1 rule

  Lyon hypothesis, Lyonization

    G-6-PD

    red-green color blindness

    anhidrotic ectodermal dysplasia

  X-inactivating center (XIC)

  X-inactive specific transcript (XIST)

    open reading frame (ORF)

Sex determination (*Drosophila*)

  non-disjunction

    XO = sterile male

    XXY = normal female

ratio (number of X chromosomes to number of haploid sets of autosomes)

    superfemale (metafemale)

    metamale

    intersex

RNA splicing, alternative splicing

dosage compensation

ZZ/ZW mode

Concepts

Sex determination

    Xy/XX, XO/XX, ZZ/ZW, *etc.*

Sex differentiation

Dosage compensation

———————————

Solutions to Problems and Discussion Questions

1. The term *heteromorphic* refers to the condition in many organisms where there are two different forms (morphs) of chromosomes such as X and Y. *Heterogamy* refers to the condition where there are two different sizes of gametes such as egg and sperm.

2. The *Protenor* form of sex determination involves the XX/XO condition while the *Lygaeus* mode involves the XX/XY condition.

3. Calvin Bridges (1916) studied nondisjunctional *Drosophila* which had a variety of sex chromosome complements. He noted that XO produced sterile males while XXY produced fertile females. It was later shown that the Y chromosome is male determining in humans. Individuals with the 47,XXY complement are males while 45,XO produces females.

In *Drosophila* it is the balance between the number of X chromosomes and the number of haploid sets of autosomes which determines sex. In humans there is a small region on the Y chromosome which determines maleness.

4. In *primary* nondisjunction half of the gametes contain two X chromosomes while the complementary gametes contain no X chromosomes. Fertilization, by a Y-bearing sperm cell, of those female gametes with two X chromosomes would produce the XXY Klinefelter syndrome. Fertilization of the "no-X" female gamete with a normal X-bearing sperm will produce the Turner syndrome.

5. (a) female $X^{rw}Y$ X male X^+X^+

F_1:	female s:	X^+Y (normal)
	males:	$X^{rw}X^+$ (normal)
F_2:	female s:	X^+Y (normal)
		$X^{rw}Y$ (reduced wing)
	males:	$X^{rw}X^+$ (normal)
		X^+X^+ (normal)

(b) female $X^{rw}X^{rw}$ X male X^+Y

F_1:	female s:	$X^{rw}X^+$ (normal)
	males:	$X^{rw}Y$ (reduced wing))
F_2:	female s:	$X^{rw}X^+$ (normal)
		$X^{rw}X^{rw}$ (reduced wing)
	males:	X^+Y (normal)
		$X^{rw}Y$ (reduced wing)

(c) No.

6. Because attached-X chromosomes have a mother-to-daughter inheritance and the father's X is transferred to the son, one would see daughters with the white eye phenotype and sons with the miniature wing phenotype.

7. Because synapsis of chromosomes in meiotic tissue is often accompanied by crossing over, it would be detrimental to sex-determining mechanisms to have sex-determining loci on the Y chromosome transferred, through crossing over, to the X chromosome.

8. A *Barr body* is a darkly staining chromosome seen in some interphase nuclei of mammals with two X chromosomes. There will be one less Barr body than number of X chromosomes. The Barr body is an X chromosome which is considered to be genetically inactive.

9. There is a simple formula for determining the number of Barr bodies in a given cell: N-1, where N is the number of X chromosomes.

Klinefelter syndrome (XXY)	= 1
Turner syndrome (XO)	= 0
47, XYY	= 0
47, XXX	= 2
48, XXXX	= 3

10. The *Lyon Hypothesis* states that the inactivation of the X chromosome occurs at random early in embryonic development. Such X chromosomes are in some way "marked" such that all progeny cells have the same X chromosome inactivated.

11. Females will display mosaic retinas with patches of defective color perception. Under these conditions, their color vision may be influenced.

12. Refer to the *Essentials* text and notice that the phenotypic mosaicism is dependent on the heterozygous condition of genes on the two X chromosomes. Dosage compensation and the formation of Barr bodies occurs only when there are two or more X chromosomes. Males normally have only one X chromosome therefore such mosaicism can not occur. Females normally have two X chromosomes. There are cases of male calico cats which are XXY.

13. Many organisms have evolved over millions of years under the fine balance of numerous gene products. Many genes required for normal cellular and organismic function in *both* males and females are located on the X chromosome. These gene products have nothing to do with sex determination or sex differentiation.

14. In mammals, the scheme of sex determination is dependent on the presence of a piece of the Y chromosome. If present a male is produced. In *Bonellia viridis*, the female proboscis produces some substance which triggers a morphological, physiological, and behavioral developmental pattern which produces males.

To elucidate the mechanism, one could attempt to isolate and characterize the active substance by testing different chemical fractions of the proboscis. Secondly, mutant analysis usually provides critical approaches into developmental processes. Depending on characteristics of the organism, one could attempt to isolate mutants which lead to changes in male or female development. Third, by using micro-tissue transplantations, one could attempt to determine which "centers" of the embryo respond to the chemical cues of the female.

15. There are several possibilities which are discussed in the *Essentials* text. One could account for the significant departures from a 1:1 ratio of males to females by suggesting that at anaphase I of meiosis, the Y chromosome more often goes to the pole which produces the more viable sperm cells. One could also speculate that the Y-bearing sperm has a higher likelihood of surviving in the female reproductive tract, or that the egg surface is more receptive to Y-bearing sperm. At this time the mechanism is unclear.

16. The presence of the Y chromosome provides a factor (or factors) which leads to the initial specification of maleness, specifically the development of testes. Subsequent expression of secondary sex characteristics must be dependent on the interaction of the normal X-linked *Tfm* allele with testosterone released from testes. Without such interaction, differentiation takes the female path. It is possible that *Tfm* produces an androgen receptor which is distributed in various pre-genital tissues. Mutations in the *Tfm* gene could knock out the supposed receptor. Using tagged antibodies to the receptor, one could establish by *in situ* antigen-antibody labeling, whether the receptor is present in mutant organisms. Interestingly, XXY male mice, heterozygous for *Tfm* show avariable protions of androgen insensitive and androgen sensitive cells due to random X inactivation.

17. Since all haploids are male and half of the egges are unfertilized, 50% of the offspring would be male at the start; adding the X_a/X_a types gives 25% more male, the remainder X_a/X_b would be female. Overall, 75% of the offspring would be male while 25% would be female.

Chapter 6: Quantitative Genetics

Concept Areas

	Coresponding Problems
Heritability	2, 10, 12, 13, 14, 15
Continuous/Discontinuous Variation	1, 3, 4, 5, 6, 9
Heredity *vs.* Environment	11
Twin Studies	7, 8

Vocabulary and Critical Issues

Processes/Methods

Discontinuous variation

Continuous variation

    quantitative inheritance

    multiple-factor (gene) hypothesis

    non-additive alleles

    additive alleles

        1:4:6:4:1

        $1/4^n$ (n = number of gene pairs)

        2n + 1 rule

polygenic

    phenotypic flexibility

    interaction with the environment

        resistance to DDT (*Drosophila*)

    RFLP analysis

Statistical analysis

    biometry

    descriptive summary

    statistical inference

        mean

        frequency distribution

        variance

        standard deviation

        standard error of the mean

Heredity vs. environment

    broad-sense heritability

    narrow-sense heritability

        heritability index (H^2)

    twin studies

        monozygotic (identical) twins

        dizygotic (fraternal) twins

        concordant vs. discordant

Mapping

    quantitative trait loci (QTL)

    non-random segregation with RFLP

Concepts

Quantitative inheritance

Complex traits

Heritability

Phenotypic variation

Heredity vs. environment

    inbred strains

    heritability index or ratio (H^2)

      broad heritability

        environmental variance

genetic variance

    interaction

    narrow-sense heritability (h^2)

      dominance variance

      additive variance

      interactive variance

Concordance

Discordance

Artificial selection

    response

    selection differential

Twin studies

Mapping

*Solutions to Problems and
Discussion Questions*

1. In *discontinuous* variation the influences of each gene pair are not additive and more typical Mendelian ratios such as 9:3:3:1 and 3:1 result. In *continuous* variation, different gene pairs interact (usually additively) to produce a phenotype which is less "stepwise" in distribution. Inheritance of a quantitative nature follows a more continuous form.

2. **(a)** *Polygenes* are those genes which are involved in determining continuously varying or multiple factor traits.

(b) *Additive alleles* are those alleles which account for the hereditary influence on the phenotype in an additive way.

(c) The *multiple factor hypothesis* suggested that many factors or genes contribute to the phenotype in a cumulative or quantitative way.

(d) *Monozygotic twins* are derived from a single fertilized egg and are thus genetically identical to each other. They provide a method for determining the influence of genetics and environment on certain traits. *Dizygotic twins* arise from two eggs fertilized by two sperm cells. They have the same genetic relationship as siblings.

The role of genetics and the role of the environment can be studied by comparing the expression of traits in monozygotic and dizygotic twins. The higher concordance value for monozygotic twins as compared to the value for dizygotic twins indicates a significant genetic component for a given trait.

(e) *Concordance* refers to the frequency with which both members of a twin pair express a given trait. *Discordance* refers to the frequency at which one twin expresses a trait while the other does not. A comparison of concordance (and discordance) frequencies can provide information on the genetic and/or environmental influence on a given trait.

(f) *Heritability* is a measure of the degree to which the phenotypic variation of a given trait is due to genetic factors. A high heritability indicates that genetic factors are major contributers to phenotypic variation while environmental factors have little impact.

3. If you add the numbers given for the ratio, you obtain the value of 16, which is indicative of a dihybrid cross. The distribution is that of a dihybrid cross with additive effects.

(a) Because a dihybrid result has been identified, there are two loci involved in the production of color. There are two alleles at each locus for a total of four alleles.

(b) Because the description of red, medium-red, etc., gives us no indication of a *quantity* of color in any form of units, we would not be able to actually quantify a unit amount for each change in color. We can say that each gene (additive allele) provides an equal *unit* amount to the phenotype and the colors differ from each other in multiples of that unit amount.

(c) The genotypes are as follows:

1/16	= dark red	=	*AABB*
4/16	= medium-dark red	=	2*AABb* 2*AaBB*
6/16	= medium red	=	*AAbb* 4*AaBb* *aaBB*
4/16	= light red	=	2*aaBb* 2*Aabb*
1/16	= white	=	*aabb*

(d) F_1 = all light red

F_2 =   1/4 medium red
2/4 light red
1/4 white

4. (a) It *is possible* that two parents of moderate height can produce offspring that are much taller or shorter than either parent because segregation can produce a variety of gametes, therefore offspring as illustrated below:

$$rrSsTtuu \quad X \quad RrSsTtUu$$
(moderate) (moderate)

Offspring from this cross can range from very tall *RrSSTTUu* (12 "tall" units) to very short *rrssttuu* (8 "small" units).

(b) If the individual with a minimum height, *rrssttuu*, is married to an individual of intermediate height *RrSsTtUu*, the offspring can be no taller than the height of the tallest parent. Notice that there is no way of having more than four dominant alleles in the offspring.

5. As you read this question, notice that the strains are inbred, therefore homozygous, and that approximately 1/250 represent the shortest and tallest groups in the F_2 generation.

(a, b) Referring to the text, see that where four gene pairs act additively, the proportion of one of the extreme phenotypes to the total number of offspring is 1/256 (add the numbers in each phenotypic class). The same may be said for the other extreme type. The extreme types in this problem are the 12cm and 36cm plants. From this observation one would suggest that there are four gene pairs involved. $(1/4^n)$

(c) If there are four gene pairs, there are nine $(2n+1)$ phenotypic categories and eight increments between these categories. Since there is a difference of 24cm between the extremes, 24cm/8 = 3cm for each increment (each of the additive alleles).

(d) A typical F_1 cross which produces a "typical" F_2 distribution would be where all gene pairs are heterozygous (*AaBbCcDd*), independently assorting, and additive. There are many possible sets of parents which would give an F_1 of this type.

The limitation is that each parent has genotypes which give a height of 24cm as stated in the problem. Because the parents are inbred, it is expected that they are fully homozygous.

An example:

$$AABBccdd \quad X \quad aabbCCDD$$

(e) Since the *aabbccdd* genotype gives a height of 12cm and each upper-case allele adds 3cm to the height, there are many possibilities for an 18 cm plant:

$$AAbbccdd,$$

$$AaBbccdd,$$

$$aaBbCcdd, \text{ etc.}$$

Any plant with seven upper-case letters will be 33cm tall:

$$AABBCCDd,$$

$$AABBCcDD,$$

$$AABbCCDD, \text{ for examples.}$$

6. (a) There is a fairly continuous range of "quantitative" phenotypes in the F_2 and an F_1 which is between the phenotypes of the two parents; thererfore, one can conclude that some phenotypic blending is occurring which is probably the result of several gene pairs acting in an additive fashion. Because the extreme phenotypes (6cm and 30cm) each represent 1/64 of the total, it is likely that there are three gene pairs in this cross.

Remember, trihybrid crosses which show independent assortment of genes have a denominator (4^3) of 64 in ratios. Also, the fact that there are seven categories of phenotypes, which, because of the relationship 2n+1 = 7, would give the number of gene pairs (n) of 3. The genotypes of the parents would be combinations of alleles which would produce a 6cm (*aabbcc*) tail and a 30cm (*AABBCC*) tail while the 18cm offspring would have a genotype of *AaBbCc*.

(b) A mating of an *AaBbCc* (for example) pig with the 6cm *aabbcc* pig would result in the following offspring:

Gametes (18cm tail)	Gamete (6cm tail)	Offspring	
ABC		AaBbCc	(18cm)
ABc		AaBbcc	(14cm)
AbC		AabbCc	(14cm)
Abc	abc	Aabbcc	(10cm)
aBC		aaBbCc	(14cm)
aBc		aaBbcc	(10cm)
abC		aabbCc	(10cm)
abc		aabbcc	(6cm)

In this example, a 1:3:3:1 ratio is the result. However, had a different 18cm tailed-pig been selected, a different ratio would occur:

$$AABbcc \ X \ aabbcc$$

Gametes (18cm tail)	Gamete (6cm tail)	Offspring
ABc	abc	AaBbcc (14cm)
Abc		Aabbcc (10cm)

7. *Monozygotic twins* are derived from a single fertilized egg and are thus genetically identical to each other. They provide a method for determining the influence of genetics and environment on certain traits. *Dizygotic twins* arise from two eggs fertilized by two sperm cells. They have the same genetic relationship as siblings.

The role of genetics and the role of the environment can be studied by comparing the expression of traits in monozygotic and dizygotic twins. The higher concordance value for monozygotic twins as compared to the value for dizygotic twins indicates a significant genetic component for a given trait.

8. For height, notice that average differences between MZ twins reared together (1.7 cm) and those MZ twins reared apart (1.8 cm) are similar (meaning little environmental influence) and considerably less than differences of DZ twins (4.4 cm) or sibs (4.5) reared together. These data indicate that genetics plays a major role in determining height.

However, for weight, notice that MZ twins reared together have a much smaller (1.9 kg) difference than MZ twins reared apart, indicating that the environment has a considerable impact on weight. By comparing the weight differences of MZ twins reared apart with DZ twins and sibs reared together, one can conclude that the environment has almost as much an influence on weight as genetics.

9. Many traits, especially those which we view as quantitative, are likely to be determined by a polygenic mode. The following are some common examples: height, general body structure, skin color, and perhaps most common behavioral traits including intelligence.

10. At first glance, this problem looks as if it will be an arithmetic headache, however, the problem can be simplified.

(a) The mean is computed by adding the measurements of all of the individuals, then dividing by the number of individuals. In this case there are 760 corn plants. To keep from having to add 760 numbers, merely multiply each height group by the number of individuals in each group. Add all the products then divide by n (760). This gives a value for the mean of 140 cm.

(b) For the variance, use the formula given below (as in the text):

$$s^2 = V = n\Sigma f(x^2) - (\Sigma fx)^2 / n(n-1)$$

To simplify the calculations, determine the square of each height group (100 cm for example) then multiply the value by the number in each group.

For the first group (100 cm) we would have:

$$100 \times 100 \times 20 = 200000$$

The rest of the groups are as follows:

$$
\begin{aligned}
110 \times 110 \times 60 &= 726000 \\
120 \times 120 \times 90 &= 1296000 \\
130 \times 130 \times 130 &= 2197000 \\
140 \times 140 \times 180 &= 3528000 \\
150 \times 150 \times 120 &= 2700000 \\
160 \times 160 \times 70 &= 1792000 \\
170 \times 170 \times 50 &= 1445000 \\
180 \times 180 \times 40 &= 1296000 \\
&= 15180000
\end{aligned}
$$

Now, the mean squared, multiplied by n is as follows:

$$140 \times 140 \times 760 = 14896000$$

Completing the calculations gives the following:

$$(15180000 - 14896000)/759$$

$$= 284000/759$$

$$= 374.18$$

(c) The *standard deviation* is the square root of the variance or 19.34.

(d) The *standard error of the mean* is the standard deviation divided by the square root of n, or about 0.70.

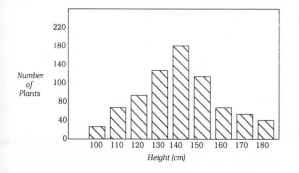

The plot approximates a normal distribution. Variation is continuous.

11. For a trait that is quantitatively measured, the relative importance of genetic *versus* environmental factors may be formally assessed by examining the heritability index (H^2 or broad heritability). In animal and plant breeding, a measure of potential response to selection based on additive variance and dominance variance is termed narrow heritability (h^2). A relatively high narrow heritability is a prediction of the impact selection may have in altering an initial randomly breeding population.

12. The formula for estimating heritability is

$$H^2 = V_G/V_P \quad \text{where } V_G \text{ and } V_P$$

are the genetic and phenotypic components of variation, respectively. The main issue in this question is obtaining some estimate of two components of phenotypic variation: genetic and environmental.

V_P is the combination of genetic and environmental variance. Because the two parental strains are inbred, they are assumed to be homozygous and the variance of 4.2 and 3.8 considered to be the result of environmental influences. The average of these two values is 4.0. The F_1 is also genetically homogeneous and gives us an additional estimation of the environmental factors.

By averaging with the parents

$$[(4.0 + 5.6)/2 = 4.8]$$

we obtain a relatively good idea of environmental impact on the phenotype. The phenotypic variance in the F_2 is the sum of the genetic (V_G) and environmental (V_E) components. We have estimated the environmental input as 4.8, so 10.3 (V_P) minus 4.8 gives us an estimate of (V_G), which is 5.5. Heritability then becomes 5.5/10.3 or 0.53. This value, when viewed in percentage form, indicates that about 53% of the variation in plant height is due to genetic influences.

13. (a) For Vitamin A

$$h_A^2 = V_A/V_P = V_A/(V_E + V_A + V_D) = 0.097$$

For Cholesterol

$$h_A^2 = 0.223$$

(b) Cholesterol content should be influenced to a greater extent by selection.

14. $h^2 = (7.5 - 8.5/6.0 - 8.5) = 0.4$

Selection will have little relative influence on olfactory learning in *Drosophila*.

15. $h^2 = 0.3 = (M_2 - 60/80 - 60)$

$$M_2 = 66 \text{ grams}$$

16. Chromosome 2 seems to confer considerable resistance to the insecticide, somewhat in the heterozygous state and more in the homozygous state. Thus, some partial dominance is occurring.

Chapter 7: Chromosome Mutations: Variation in Number and Arrangement

Concept Areas	Corresponding Problems
Variation in Chromosome Number	1, 2, 3, 4, 5, 6, 7, 8, 15, 16, 17, 19, 20, 21, 22, 26, 27
Deletions	9
Duplications	9, 12, 13
Inversions	10, 11, 14, 18, 23, 24, 25
Translocations	14

Vocabulary and Critical Issues

Structures and Substances

Colchicine

Protoplast

rDNA

Nucleolar organizer (NOR)

Micronuclei

Processes/ Methods

Chromosome mutations (aberrations)

aneuploidy(F7.1)

nondisjunction

monosomy, trisomy, tetrasomy, pentasomy

Klinefelter syndrome

Turner syndrome

haplo-IV (*Drosophila*)

partial monosomy

segmental deletions

cri-du-chat syndrome, 46,5p-

trisomy

XXX (*Drosophila*, humans)

Datura

Oryza ativa

Down syndrome (G group)

trisomy 21 (47, 21+)

maternal age

genetic counseling

amniocentesis

chorionic villus sampling (CVS)

familial Down syndrome

Patau syndrome (D group)

trisomy 13 (47, 13+)

Edwards syndrome (E group)

trisomy 18 (47, 18+)

reduced viability

embryos

spontaneously aborted fetuses

euploidy (F7.1)

diploid (2n)

polyploid

triploid (3n)

tetraploid (4n)

pentaploid (5n)

autopolyploidy

autotriploids (3n)

complete nondisjunction

dispermic fertilization

tetraploid X diploid

autotetraploids (4n)

cold or heat shock

allopolyploidy

hybridization

allotetraploid (amphidiploid)

(cotton, *Triticale*)

Raphanus X *Brassica*

Chromosome structure

deletions (deficiency)

terminal, intercalary

loop (deficiency, compensation)

pseudodominance

duplications

gene redundancy

rDNA

bobbed

gene amplification

nucleolar organizer (NOR)

micronucleoli

Bar eye in *Drosophila*

semidominant

position effect

evolutionary aspects

gene families

rearrangements

inversions

paracentric

pericentric

heterozygotes

inversion loops

dicentric chromatids

acentric chromatids

dicentric bridges

"suppression of crossing over"

translocations

reciprocal

unorthodox synapsis

semisterility

familial Down syndrome

Robertsonian fusion

14/21 or D/G

fragile sites

X chromosome

Martin-Bell syndrome (MBS)

fragile X syndrome

trinucleotide repeats

genetic anticipation

cancer

FMIT

Concepts

Significance of variation in chromosomes

genomic balance

sex chromosome balance

evolution

Gene duplication (evolutionary aspects)

sequence homology

Inversions

"suppression of crossing over"

Translocations

Fragile sites

F7.1. Illustration of the chromosomal configurations of duploid and aneuploid genomes of *Drosophila melanogaster*.

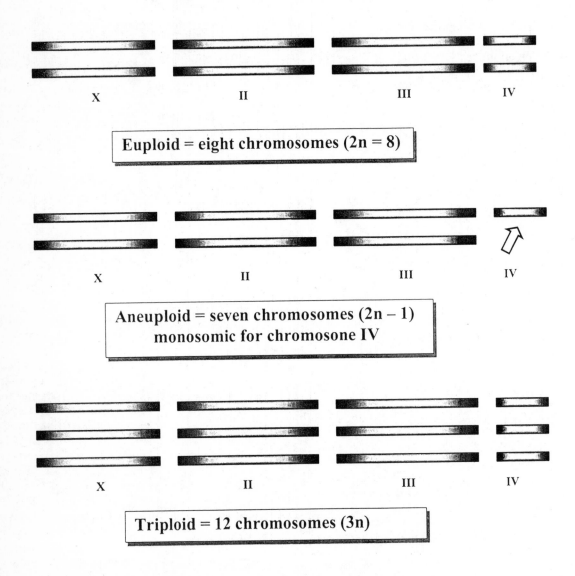

Drosophila melanogaster female

Euploid = eight chromosomes (2n = 8)

Aneuploid = seven chromosomes (2n – 1)
monosomic for chromosone IV

Triploid = 12 chromosomes (3n)

Solutions to Problems
and Discussion Questions

1. With a diploid chromosome number of 18 (2n), a haploid (n) would have nine chromosomes, a triploid (3n) would have 27 chromosomes, and a tetraploid (4n) would have 36 chromosomes. A trisomic would have one extra chromosome (19) and a monosomic one less than the diploid (17).

2. With frequent exceptions especially in plants, organisms typically inherit one chromosome complement (*haploid = n =* one representative from each homologous pair of chromosomes) from each parent. Such organisms are *diploid*, or 2n. When an organism contains complete multiples of the *n* complement (3n, 4n, 5n, etc.) it is said to be *euploid* in contrast to *aneuploid* in which complete haploid sets do not occur. An example of an aneuploid is *trisomic* where a chromosome is added to the 2n complement. In humans, a trisomy 21 would be symbolized as 2n+1 or 47,+21.

Monosomy is an aneuploid condition in which one member of a chromosome pair is missing, thus producing the chromosomal formula of 2n-1. Haplo-IV is an example of monosomy in *Drosophila*. *Trisomy* is the chromosomal condition of 2n+1 where an extra chromosome is present. Down syndrome is an example in humans (47, 21+). See the *Essentials* text and notice that all the chromosomes are present in the diploid state except chromosome #21.

Patau syndrome is a chromosomal condition where there is an extra D group chromosome. Such individuals are 47,13+ and have multiple congenital malformations. *Edwards syndrome* is a chromosomal condition where there is an extra E group chromosome (47,18+). Individuals with Edwards syndrome have multiple congenital malformations and reduced life expectancy.

Polyploidy refers to instances where there are more than two haploid sets of chromosomes in an individual cell. *Autopolyploidy* refers to cases of polyploidy where all the chromosomes in the individual originate from the same species.

Allopolyploidy involves instances where the chromosomes originate from the hybridization of two different species, usually closely related.

In *paracentric* inversions, the centromere is not included in the region bounded by the breakpoints whereas in *pericentric* inversions, the breakpoints include the centromere.

3. Individuals with Down syndrome, while suffering congenital defects, tendencies toward respiratory disease and leukemia, can live well into adulthood. Individuals with Patau or Edwards syndrome live less than four months on the average. Comparing the different sizes of the involved chromosomes (21, 13, and 18, respectively) in the *Essentials* text for example, suggests that the larger the chromosome, the lower the likelihood of lengthy survival. In addition, it would be expected that certain chromosomes, because of their genetic content, may have different influences on development.

4. The fact that there is a significant maternal age effect associated with Down syndrome indicates that nondisjunction in older females contributes disproportionately to the number of Down syndrome individuals. In addition, certain genetic and cytogenetic marker data indicate the influence of female nondisjunction.

5. While several trisomies (for chromosomes 21, 18, 13, the X and Y) are tolerated, monosomy for the autosomes is not tolerated. Karyotypic analysis of spontaneously aborted fetuses has indicated a relatively large degree of departures from the typical diploid state. The delicate genetic balance produced by millions of years of evolution must be maintained in order for any organism (but especially animals) to develop normally. Monosomy leads to the exposure of recessive, deleterious genes thus producing developmental abnormalities. Dosage compensation of the sex chromosomes and the relative paucity of Y-linked genes probably contribute to the survival of sex-chromosome aneuploidy. Notice how large the X chromosome is compared with other chromosomes.

At least 20 percent of all conceptions are terminated in natural abortion. Of these, thirty percent show some chromosomal anomaly. Of the chromosomal anomalies that occur, approximately ninety percent are eliminated by spontaneous abortion.

Trisomy for every human chromosome has been observed, however, monosomy, the reciprocal meiotic event of trisomy, is rare. This observation probably results from gamete or early embryonic inviability.

6. Because an allotetraploid has a possibility of producing bivalents at meiosis I, it would be considered the most fertile of the three. Having an even number of chromosomes to match up at the metaphase I plate, autotetraploids would be considered to be more fertile than autotriploids.

7. The sterility of interspecific hybrids is often caused from a high proportion of univalents in meiosis I. As such, viable gametes are rare and the likelihood of two such gametes "meeting" is remote. Even if partial homology of chromosomes allows some pairing, sterility is usually the rule. The horticulturist may attempt to reverse the sterility by treating the sterile hybrid with colchicine. Such a treatment, if sucessful, may double the chromosome number and each chromosome would now have a homologue with which to pair during meiosis.

8. American cultivated cotton has 26 pairs of chromosomes; 13 large, 13 small. Old world cotton has 13 pairs of large chromosomes and American wild cotton has 13 pairs of small chromosomes. It is likely that an interspecific hybridization occurred followed by chromosome doubling. These events probably produced a fertile amphidiploid (allotetraploid). Experiments have been conducted to reconstruct the origin of American cultivated cotton.

9. Basically the synaptic configurations produced by chromosomes bearing a deletion or duplication (on one homologue) are very similar. There will be point-for-point pairing in all sections which are capable of pairing. The section which has no homologue will "loop out" as in the *Essentials* text.

10. While there is the appearance that crossing over is suppressed in inversion "heterozygotes" the phenomenon extends from the fact that the crossover chromatids end up being abnormal in genetic content. As such they fail to produce viable (or competitive) gametes or lead to zygotic or embryonic death. Notice in the *Essentials* text the crossover chromatids end up genetically unbalanced.

11. Examine the *Essentials* text and notice that in (a) there are two genetically balanced chromatids (normal and inverted) and two, those resulting from a single crossover in the inversion loop, which are genetically unbalanced and abnormal (dicentric and acentric). The dicentric chromatid will often break, thereby producing highly abnormal fragments whereas the acentric fragment is often lost in the meiotic process. In part (b) all the chromatids have centromeres, but the two chromatids involved in the crossover are genetically unbalanced. The balanced chromatids are of normal or inverted sequence.

12. In a work entitled *Evolution by Gene Duplication*, Ohno, suggests that gene duplication has been essential in the origin of new genes. If gene products serve essential functions, mutation and therefore evolution, would not be possible unless these gene products could be compensated for by products of duplicated, normal genes. The duplicated genes, or the original genes themselves, would be able to undergo mutational "experimentation" without necessarily threatening the survival of the ogranism.

13. A Turner syndrome female has the sex chromosome composition of XO. If the father had hemophilia it is likely that the Turner syndrome individual inherited the X chromosome from the father and no sex chromosome from the mother. If nondisjunction occurred in the mother, either during meiosis I or meiosis II, an egg with no X chromosome can be the result. See the *Essentials* text for a diagram of primary and secondary nondisjunction.

14. The primrose, *Primula kewensis*, with its 36 chromosomes, is likely to have formed from the hybridization and subsequent chromosome doubling of a cross between the two other species, each with 18 chromosomes. An example of this type of allotetraploidy (amphidiploidy) is seen in the *Essentials* text.

15. Given the basic chromosome set of nine unique chromosomes (a haploid complement) other forms with the "n multiples" are forms of autotetraploidy. In the illustration below the n basic set is multiplied to various levels as is the autotetraploid in the example.

Basic set of nine unique chromosomes (n)

— — — — — — — — — —

↓

Autotetraploid (4n)

Individual organisms with 27 chromosomes (3n) are more likely to be sterile because there are trivalents at meiosis I which cause a relatively high number of unbalanced gametes to be formed.

16. Set up the cross in the usual manner, realizing that recessive genes in the Haplo-IV individual will be expressed.

Let b = bent bristles; b^+ = normal bristles

(a)

_/b   X   b⁺/b⁺ —>
F₁:
_/b⁺   = normal bristles
b /b⁺   = normal bristles

F₂:

    _/b⁺ X   b /b⁺   —>

    _/b⁺   = normal bristles
    _/b   = bent bristles
    b⁺/b⁺   = normal bristles
    b/b⁺   = normal bristles

(b)

    _/b⁺ X   b/b   —>

F₁:

    _/b   = bent bristles
    b /b⁺   = normal bristles

F₂:

    _/b   X   b /b⁺   —>

    _/b⁺   = normal bristles
    _/b   = bent bristles
    b⁺/b   = normal bristles
    b /b   = bent bristles

17. The cross would be as follows:

$$WWWW \text{ X } wwww$$

(assuming that chromosomes pair as bivalents at meiosis)

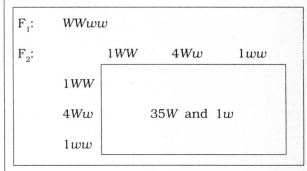

F₁: WWww

F₂:

	1WW	4Ww	1ww
1WW			
4Ww		35W and 1w	
1ww			

18. **(a)** In all probability, crossing over in the inversion loop of an inversion (in the heterozygous state) had produced defective, unbalanced chromatids, thus leading to stillbirths and/or malformed children. **(b)** It is probable that a significant proportion (perhaps 50%) of the children of the man will be similarly influenced by the inversion. **(c)** Since the karyotypic abnormality is observable, it may be possible to detect some of the abnormal chromosomes of the fetus by amniocentesis or CVS. However, depending on the type of inversion and the ability to detect minor changes in banding patterns, all abnormal chromosomes may not be detected.

19. Considering that there are at least three map units between each of the loci, and that only four phenotypes are observed, it is likely that genes *a b c d* are included in an inversion and crossovers which do occur among these genes are not recovered because of their genetically unbalanced nature. In a sense, the minimum distance between loci *d* and *e* can be estimated as 10 map units

$$(48 + 52/1000);$$

However, this is actually the distance from the *e* locus to the breakpoint which includes the inversion.

The "map" is therefore as drawn below:

20. **(a)** Reciprocal translocation

(b)

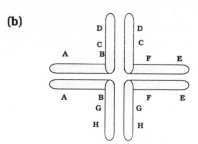

(c) Notice that all chromosomal segments are present and there is no apparent loss of chromosomal material. However, if the breakpoints for the translocation occurred within genes then an abnormal phenotype may be the result. In addition, a gene's function is sometimes influenced by its position; its neighbors in other words. If such "position effects" occur then a different phenotype may result.

(d) It is likely that the translocation is the cause of the miscarriages. Segregation of the chromosomal elements will produce approximately half unbalanced gametes. The chance of a normal child is approximately one in two, however half of the normal children will be translocation carriers. Sometimes, depending on the breakpoints of the translocation, genetically unbalanced children are carried to term. In many such cases, they suffer from developmental abnormalities.

...The genetic circumstances result from the reciprocal translocation which then causes unbalanced chromosomal complements to be present in embryos. Such genetically unbalanced embryos fail to thrive.

...This question is difficult to answer given the possibility that she may well have some healthy children. It all depends on segregation patterns of the chromosomes. Information is provided by the genetic counselor, but the final decision in these types of cases must rest with the couple involved.

...The chance of having a genetically balanced child would be approximately 0.5. However, half of that 0.5 will be translocation carriers.

Chapter 8: Linkage and Chromosome Mapping in Eukaryotes

Concept Areas	**Corresponding Problems**
Linkage Detection	5, 6, 12, 15
Mapping	4, 9, 10, 11, 13, 14
Double Crossover	7
Factors Influencing Crossovers	1, 2, 3
Interference	8

Vocabulary and Critical Issues

Structures and Substances

Linkage groups

Drosophila

Neurospora

Chlamydomonas

tetrad

Zea mays

Chiasma

Heterokaryon

Synkaryon

Ascospores

Ascus (pl. asci)

Bromodeoxyuridine (BUdR)

Processes/Methods

Linkage and crossing over

crossover gametes (recombinant)

parental gametes

recombination

reciprocal classes

complete

incomplete

chiasmata (chiasma)

three-point mapping

product rule (multiple crossovers)

non-crossovers (NCO)

single crossovers (SCO)

double crossovers (DCO)

Determining gene sequence

interference

coefficient of coincidence

Gene to centromere mapping

first division segregation

second division segregation

$$\frac{1/2(\text{second-division segregant asci})}{\text{total asci scored}}$$

Concepts

Cytological evidence (crossing over)

cytological markers

lod score method

Somatic cell hybridization

random loss of human chromosomes

synteny testing

Haploid organisms

tetrad analysis

Sister chromatid exchange

bromodeoxyuridine (BUdR)

harlequin chromosomes

Bloom syndrome

Mendel and linkage

independent assortment

Linked genes (linkage groups)

arrangement (F8.1)

Chromosome maps

Linkage ratio

map unit (% recombination)

deviation from a 1:1:1:1

centimorgan (cM)

50% maximum

Interference

coefficient of coincidence

expected frequency of DCO

observed frequency of DCO

positive interference

Generation of variation

Cytological evidence for crossing over

Mendel and linkage considerations

F8.1. Illustration of two typical configurations of two heterozygous gene pairs. Understanding of such arrangements is key to doing linkage problems.

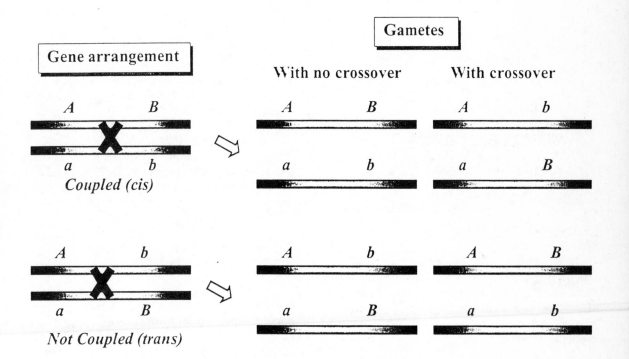

Solutions to Problems and Discussion Questions

1. With some qualification, one can say that crossing over is randomly distributed over the length of the chromosome. Two loci which are far apart are more likely to have a crossover between them than two loci that are close together.

↑ = crossover

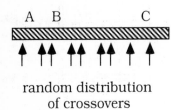

random distribution
of crossovers

2. As mentioned above with some qualifications, crossovers occur randomly along the lengths of chromosomes. Within any region, the occurrence of two events is less likely than the occurrence of one event. If the probability of one event is

$$1/X,$$

the probability of two events occurring at the same time will be

$$1/X^2.$$

3. Each cross must be set-up in such a way as to reveal crossovers because it is on the basis of crossover frequency that genetic maps are developed. It is necessary that genetic heterogeneity exist so that different arrangements of genes, generated by crossing over, can be distinguished.

The organism which is heterozygous must be the sex in which crossing over occurs. In other words, it would be useless to map genes in *Drosophila* if the male parent is the heterozygote since crossing over is not typical in *Drosophila* males.

Lastly, the cross must be setup so that the phenotypes of the offspring readily reveal their genotypes. The best arrangement is one where a fully heterozygous organism is crossed with an organism which is fully recessive for the genes being mapped.

4. Since the distance between *dp* and *ap* is greatest, they must be on the "outside" and *cl* must be in the middle. The genetic map would be as *follows:*

$$dp—cl———————ap$$
$$3\,mu. \qquad 39\,mu.$$

5. In looking at this problem one can immediately conclude that the two loci (kernel color and plant color) are linked because the test cross progeny occur in a ratio other than 1:1:1:1 (and epistasis does not appear because all phenotypes expected are present). The question is whether the arrangement in the parents is *coupled* (see F8.1)

$$RY/ry \quad X \quad ry/ry$$

or *not coupled* (see F6.1)

$$Ry/rY \quad X \quad ry/ry$$

Notice that the most frequent phenotypes in the offspring, the parentals, are colored, green (88) and colorless, yellow (92). This indicates that the heterozygous parent in the test cross is *coupled*

$$RY/ry \quad X \quad ry/ry$$

with the two dominant genes on one chromosome and the two recessives on the homologue (F6.1). Seeing that there are 20 crossover progeny among the 200, or 20/200, the map distance would be 10 map units (20/200 X 100 to convert to percentages) between the R and Y loci.

6. Since there is no indication as to the configuration of the P and Z genes (*coupled* or *not coupled*) in the parent, one must look at the percentages in the offspring. Notice that the most frequent classes are PZ and pz. These classes represent the parental (non-crossover) groups, which indicates that the original parental arrangement in the test cross was

$$PZ/pz \quad X \quad pz/pz$$

Adding the crossover percentages together

$$(6.9 + 7.1) \text{ gives } 14\%$$

which would be the map distance between the two genes.

7.

	female A:	female B:	Frequency:
NCO	3, 4	7, 8	first
SCO	1, 2	3, 4	second
SCO	7, 8	5, 6	third
DCO	5, 6	1, 2	fourth

The single crossover classes which represent crossovers between the genes that are closer together (*d-b*) would occur less frequently than the classes of crossovers between more distant genes (*b-c*).

8. For two reasons, it is clear that the genes are in the *coupled* configuration (see F6.1) in the F_1 female. First, a completely homozygous female was mated to a wild type male and second, the phenotypes of the offspring indicate the following parental classes

$$sc \ s \ v \text{ and } + + +$$

(a)

P_1:

$$sc \ s \ v \ /sc \ s \ v \quad X \quad + + +/Y$$

F_1:

$$+ + +/sc \ s \ v \quad X \quad sc \ s \ v/Y$$

(b) For determining the sequence of genes, examine the parental classes and compare the arrangement with the double crossover (least frequent) classes. Notice that the v gene "switches places" between the two groups (parentals and double crossovers). The gene which switches places is in the middle.

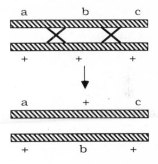

The map distances are determined by first writing the proper arrangement and sequence of genes, then computing the distances between each set of genes.

$$\frac{sc \quad v \quad s}{+ \quad + \quad +}$$

$$sc - v \quad = \frac{150 + 156 + 10 + 14}{1000} \quad X \ 100$$

$$= 33\% \text{ (map units)}$$

$$v - s \quad = \frac{46 + 30 + 10 + 14}{1000} \quad X \ 100$$

$$= 10\% \text{ (map units)}$$

Double crossovers are always added into each crossover group because they represent a crossover in each region.

$$sc\text{———}v\text{———}s$$
$$\quad\quad 33\quad\quad 10$$

(c) The coefficient of coincidence=

$$\frac{\text{observed freq. double C/O}}{\text{expected freq. double C/O}}$$

$$=\quad\frac{(14+10)/1000}{.33\ X\ .1}$$

$$=\quad\frac{.024}{.033}$$

$$=\quad.727$$

which indicates that there were fewer double crossovers than expected, therefore positive chromosomal interference is present.

9. (a) The cross will be as follows. Represent the *Dichete* gene as an upper-case letter because it is dominant.

P_1:

$$D\ +\ +/\ +\ +\ +\quad X\quad +\ e\ p/+\ e\ p$$

F_1:

$$D\ +\ +/+\ e\ p\quad X\quad +\ e\ p/+\ e\ p$$

F_2:

$D\ +\ +/+\ e\ p$	Dichete
$+\ e\ p\ /+\ e\ p$	ebony, pink
$D\ e\ +/+\ e\ p$	Dichete, ebony
$+\ +\ p/+\ e\ p$	pink
$D\ +\ p/+\ e\ p$	Dichete, pink
$+\ e\ +/+\ e\ p$	ebony
$D\ e\ p/+\ e\ p$	Dichete, ebony, pink
$+\ +\ +/+\ e\ p$	wild type

(b) Determine which gene is in the middle by comparing the parental classes with the double crossover classes. Notice that the *pink* gene "switches places" between the two groups (parentals and double crossovers). The gene which switches places is in the middle. So rewriting the sequence of genes with the correct arrangement gives the following:

F_1:

$$D\ +\ +/+\ p\ e\quad X\quad +\ p\ e/+\ p\ e$$

Distances: remember to add in the double crossover classes

$$D\text{-}p\quad =\ \frac{12\ +\ 13\ +\ 2\ +\ 3}{1000}\ X\quad 100$$

$$=\ 3.0\text{ map units}$$

$$p\text{-}e\quad =\ \frac{84\ +\ 96\ +\ 2\ +\ 3}{1000}\ X\quad 100$$

$$=\ 18.5\text{ map units}$$

10. The map distance of a gene to the centromere in *Neurospora* is determined by dividing the percentage of second division asci (tetrads) by two. Patterns other than *BBbb* or *bbBB* are "second division" as discussed in the text and represent a crossover between the gene in question and the centromere. In the data given, the percentage of second division segregation is 20/100 or 20%. Dividing by 2 (because only two of the four chromatids are involved in any single crossover event) gives 10 map units.

11. First make a drawing with the genes placed on the homologous chromosomes as follows:

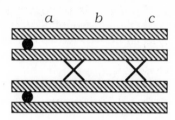

Realize that there are four chromatids in each tetrad and a single crossover involves only two of the four chromatids. The non-involved chromatids must be added to the non-crossover classes. Do all the crossover classes first, then add up the non-crossover chromatids.

For example, in the first crossover class (20 between *a* and *b*) notice that there will be 40 chromatids which were not involved in the crossover. These 40 must be added to the *abc* and +++ classes.

a	*b*	*c*	=	168
+	+	+	=	168
a	+	+	=	20
+	*b*	*c*	=	20
+	+	*c*	=	10
a	*b*	+	=	10
+	*b*	+	=	2
a	+	*c*	=	2

The map distances would be computed as follows:

$$a - b = \frac{20 + 20 + 2 + 2}{400} \times 100$$

$$= 11 \text{ map units}$$

$$b - c = \frac{10 + 10 + 2 + 2}{400} \times 100$$

$$= 6 \text{ map units}$$

12. Since *Stubble* is a dominant mutation (and homozygous lethal) one can determine whether it is heterozygous (*Sb/+*) or homozygous wild type (*+/+*). One would use the typical test cross arrangement with the *curled* gene so the arrangement would be

$$+ \; cu/ + \; cu$$

13. This set-up involves an F_1 in which the fully heterozygous female has the genes *y* and *w* in *coupled* and *ct* in *not coupled*. The arrangement for the cross is therefore:

(a) $\qquad y \; w \; +/+ \; + \; ct \quad X \quad y \; w \; +/Y$

It is important at this point to determine the gene sequence. Examine the parental classes and compare the arrangement with the double crossover (least frequent) classes. Notice that the *w* gene "switches places" between the two groups (parentals and double crossovers). The gene which switches places is in the middle. Therefore the arrangement as written above is correct.

(b)

$$y - w = \frac{9 + 6 + 0 + 0}{1000} \times 100$$

$$= 1.5 \text{ map units}$$

$$w - ct = \frac{90 + 95 + 0 + 0}{1000} \times 100$$

$$= 18.5 \text{ map units}$$

$$\underset{0.0}{y} \rule{1cm}{0.4pt} \underset{1.5}{w} \rule{2cm}{0.4pt} \underset{20.0}{ct}$$

(c) There were

$$.185 \; X \; .015 \; X \; 1000 = 2.775$$

double crossovers expected.

(d) Because the cross to the F_1 males included the normal (wild type) gene for *cut wings* it would not be possible to unequivocally determine the genotypes from the F_2 phenotypes for all classes.

14. This problem can be approached by looking for the most distant loci (*adp* and *b*) then filling in the intermediate loci. In this case the map for parts **(a)** and **(b)** is the following:

d	*b*	*pr*	*vg*	*c*	*adp*
31	48	54	67	75	83

Map Units

The expected map units between *d* and *c* would be 44, *d* and *vg* would be 36, and *d* and *adp* 52, however because there is a theoretical maximum of 50 map units possible between two loci in any one cross, that distance would be below the 52 determined by simple subtraction.

15. **(a)** $2^n = 8$

(b) 2 (no crossing over)

(c) *A* and *B* loci are 20 map units apart and assort independently from *C*.

16. (a) There are several ways to think through this problem. Remember that there is no crossing over in *Drosophila* males, therefore any gene on the same chromosome will be completely linked to any other gene on the same chromosome. Since you can get *pink* by itself, *short* cannot be completely linked to it. This leaves linkage to *black* on the second chromosome, the 4th chromosome, or the X chromosome. Since the distribution of phenotypes in males and females is essentially the same, the gene cannot be X-linked. In addition, the F_1 males were wild and if the *short* gene is on the X, the F_1 males would be short.

It is also reasonable to state that the gene can not be on the 4th chromosome because there would be eight phenotypic classes (independent assortment of three genes) instead of the four observed. Through these insights, one could conclude that the *short* gene is on chromosome 2 with the *black* gene.

Another way to approach this problem is to make three chromosomal configurations possible in the F_1 male. By producing gametes from this male, the answer becomes obvious.

Case A	Case B	Case C
p b sh	*p sh b*	*b sh p*
+ + +	+ + +	+ + +

Develop the gametes from Case C and cross them out to the completely recessive triple mutant. You will get the results in the table.

(b) The parental cross is now the following:

Females: *b sh p*   X   Males: *b sh p*
              + + +   *b sh p*

The new gametes resulting from crossing over in the female would be *b* + and + *sh*. Since the gene *p* is assorting independently, it is not important in this discussion. Because 15% of the offspring now contain these recombinant chromatids, the map distance between the two genes must be 15.

82

Chapter 9: Mapping in Bacteria and Bacteriophages

Concept Areas	Corresponding Problems
Bacterial Mutation and Growth	11
Genetic Recombination in Bacteria	1,
Conjugation	2, 3, 4, 5, 6, 7, 14
Transformation	12
Bacteriophages	9, 10,
Transduction	8
Mutation and Recombination in Viruses	13

Vocabulary and Critical Issues

Structures and Substances

Spontaneous mutations

Growth conditions

    minimal medium

    liquid culture

    Petri dish

    prototroph

    auxotroph

Donor strain

    E. coli K12

    F sex pilus

    fertility factor, F factor

    RecA, B, C, D proteins

    rec genes

    lysozyme

    Hfr

circular chromosome

F', merozygotes

    partial diploid

Plasmids

    F factors

    R plasmids

    resistance transfer factor (RTF)

    r-determinants

    antibiotic resistance

Col plasmids

    ColE1

    colicins

    colicinogenic

Bacteriophage T4

Protein capsid

Lysozyme

Plaque

Episome

Prophage P22

Processes/Methods

Sensitive, Resistant

    lag, log, stationary phases

Bacterial recombination

    conjugation

        F^+, F^-

        physical contact

        unidirectional

        donor, recipient

        high frequency recombination, Hfr

            ordered transfer

            interrupted mating technique

            circular map

F' state

    merozygotes

Recombination

Transformation

    competence

    heteroduplex

    linkage

    cotransformation

Transduction

      phage life cycle

virulent phage

    plaque (plaque assay)

      lysis

  lysogeny

      temperate phage

      symbiotic relationship

      prophage

      lysogenic bacterium

      U-tube experiment

         filterable agent (FA)

         prophage P22

      generalized transduction

        abortive transduction

        complete transduction

    cotransduction

    mapping

Mutations (viral)

    rapid lysis, host range

    mixed infection experiments

    E. coli B, K12

Concepts

Adaptation hypothesis

Fluctuation test

Dilution

Bacterial recombination - all forms

    relationship to *rec* genes

Mapping

Solutions to Problems and Discussion Questions

1. Three modes of recombination in bacteria are *conjugation, transformation,* and *transduction.* Conjugation is dependent on the F factor which, by a variety of mechanisms, can direct genetic exchange between two bacterial cells. Transformation is the uptake of exogenous DNA by cells. Transduction is the exchange of genetic material using a bacteriophage.

2. (a) The requirement for physical contact between bacterial cells during conjugation was established by placing a filter in a U-tube so that the medium can be exchanged but the bacteria cannot come in contact. Under this condition, conjugation does not occur.

(b) By treating cells with streptomycin, an antibiotic, it was shown that recombination would not occur if one of the two bacterial strains was inactivated. However, if the other was similarly treated, recombination would occur. Thus, directionality was suggested, with one strain being a donor strain and the other being the recipient.

(c) An F$^+$ bacterium contains a circular, double-stranded, structurally independent, DNA molecule which can direct recombination. In Hfr cells, the F factor is integrated into the bacterial chromosome.

3. (a) In an F$^+$ X F$^-$ cross, the transfer of the F factor produces a recipient bacterium which is F$^+$. Any gene may be transferred, and the frequency of transfer is relatively low. Crosses which are Hfr X F$^-$ produce recombinants at a higher frequency than the F$^+$ X F$^-$ cross. The transfer is oriented (non-random) and the recipient cell remains F$^-$.

(b) Bacteria which are F$^+$ possess the F factor, while those that are F$^-$ lack the F factor. In Hfr cells, the F factor is integrated into the bacterial chromosome and in F' bacteria, the F factor is free of the bacterial chromosome yet possesses a piece of the bacterial chromosome.

4. Mapping the chromosome in an Hfr X F$^-$ cross takes advantage of the oriented transfer of the bacterial chromosome through the conjugation tube. For each F type, the point of insertion and the direction of transfer are fixed, therefore breaking the conjugation tube at different times produces partial diploids with corresponding portions of the donor chromosome being transferred. The length of the chromosome being transferred is contingent on the duration of conjugation, thus mapping of genes is based on time.

5. One can approach this problem by lining up the data from the various crosses in the following order:

Hfr Strain	Order
1	T C H R O >>
2	H R O M B >>
3	<< C H R O M
4	M B A K T>>
5	<< B A K T C

TCHROMBAK

Notice that all of the genes can be linked together to give a consistent map and that the ends overlap, indicating that the map is circular. The order is reversed in two of the crosses, indicating the orientation of transfer is reversed.

6. In an Hfr X F$^-$ cross, the F factor is directing the transfer of the donor chromosome. It takes approximately 90 minutes to transfer the entire chromosome. Because the F factor is the last element to be transferred and the conjugation tube is fragile, the likelihood for complete transfer is low.

7. The F$^+$ element can enter the host bacterial chromosome and upon returning to its independent state, it may pick up a piece of a bacterial chromosome. When combined with a bacterium with a complete chromosome, a partial diploid, or merozygote, is formed.

8. In their experiment a filter was placed between the two auxotrophic strains which would not allow contact. F-mediated conjugation requires contact and without that contact, such conjugation can not occur. The treatment with DNase showed that the filterable agent was not naked DNA.

9. A *plaque* results when bacteria in a "lawn" are infected by a phage and the progeny of the phage destroy (lyse) the bacteria. A somewhat clear region is produced which is called a plaque.

Lysogeny is a complex process whereby certain temperate phage can enter a bacterial cell and instead of following a lytic developmental path, integrate their DNA into the bacterial chromosome. In doing so, the bacterial cell becomes lysogenic. The latent, integrated phage chromosome is called a *prophage.*

10. Starting with a single bacteriophage, one lytic cycle produces 200 progeny phage, three more lytic cycles would produce $(200)^4$ or 1,600,000,000 phage.

11. (a) Culture #1 represents a cell concentration of 240 cells/ml X 10^9 (recall that only 0.1ml of the various dilutions was plated) which had been irradiated. Because leucine is added to the minimal medium, both *leu*$^+$ and *leu*$^-$ cells will grow.

Culture #2 represents a cell concentration of 120 cells/ml X 10^2 which had been irradiated. Because leucine is not added to the minimal medium, only *leu*$^+$ cells will grow.

Culture #3 represents a cell concentration of 120 cells/ml X 10^9 which had not been irradiated. Because leucine is added to the minimal medium, both *leu*$^+$ and *leu*$^-$ cells will grow.

Culture #4 represents a cell concentration of 30 cells/ml X 10^1 which had not been irradiated. Because leucine is not added to the minimal medium, only *leu*$^+$ cells will grow. One would expect the values to be similar in cultures #1 and #3 because, with leucine added to the medium, one cannot differentiate between *leu*$^+$ and *leu*$^-$ cells.

However, it is likely that new non-leucine related nutritional mutations might be induced by the irradiation. If anything, we might expect to see fewer colonies from culture #1 when compared to #3. The difference of **240 cells/ml** X 10^9 and **120 cells/ml** X 10^9 may be within the limits of experimental error.

(b) The general formula for determining mutation rate is to divide the number of mutant bacteria by the total number of bacteria. In this experiment the spontaneous mutation rate would be calculated as follows:

$$(30 \text{ X } 10^1)/(120 \text{ X } 10^9) = 0.25 \text{ X } 10^{-8}$$

The induced mutation rate would be calculated as follows:

$$(120 \text{ X } 10^2)/(240 \text{ X } 10^9) = 0.5 \text{ X } 10^{-7}$$

12. Notice that the incorporation of loci a^+ and b^+ occurs much more frequently than the incorporation of b^+ and c^+ together (210 to 1) and the incorporation of all three genes $a^+b^+c^+$ occurs relatively infrequently. If a and b loci are close together and both are far from locus c, then fewer crossovers would be required to incorporate the two linked loci compared to all three loci. If all three loci were close together, then the frequency of incorporation of all three would be similar to the frequency of incorporation of any two contiguous loci, which is not the case.

13. The first problem to be solved is the gene order. Clearly, the parental types are

$$a^+b^+c^+ \text{ and } a^-b^-c^-$$

because they are the most frequent. The double crossover types are the least frequent,

$$a^-b^-c^+ \text{ and } a^+b^+c^-.$$

Because it is the gene in the middle that switches places when one compares the parental and double crossover classes, the *c* gene must be in the middle. The map distances are as follows:

a to c = (740 + 670 +90 +110)/10,000

= 16.1 map units

c to b = (160 + 140 +90 +110)/10,000

= 5 map units

To determine the type of interference, first determine the *expected* frequency of double crossovers (0.161 X .05 = .000805), which when multiplied by 10,000 gives approximately 80. The *observed* number of double crossovers is 90 + 110 or 200. Since many more double crossovers are observed than expected, negative interference is occurring.

14. **(a)** When nutrients A and B are added, selection is for *c*. When nutrients B and C are added, selection is for *a*. When nutrients A and C are added, selection is for *b*.

(b) <u>   *b a*   *c*   F</u>

Chapter 10: DNA - Structure and Analysis

Concept Areas	Corresponding Problems
Central Dogma of Biology	1, 2
Evidence (DNA is Genetic Material)	3, 5
Structure of DNA/RNA	7, 8, 9, 10, 11, 12, 15, 16, 17
Mutation	18, 19
RNA as Genetic Material	6
Differential Labeling	4
Molecular Hybridization	13, 14,20

Vocabulary and Critical Issues

Historical

Miescher (nuclein) - 1868

  genetic material

    proteins

    nucleic acids,

      tetranucleotide hypothesis

      base ratios

        Erwin Chargaff (1940s)

      transforming principle

        Griffith (1927)

        Avery *et al.* (1944)

    T2 bacteriophage (phage)

      Hershey and Chase (1952)

        ^{32}P, ^{35}S

    Watson and Crick (1953)
      Franklin, Wilkins

Structures and Substances

Messenger RNA (mRNA)

Transfer RNA (tRNA)

Ribosomal RNA (rRNA)

  ribosome

Proteolytic enzymes

Ribonuclease, Deoxyribonuclease

Protoplasts (spheroplasts)

Reverse transcriptase

Nucleic acids

  nucleotide

  pentose sugar (ribose, deoxyribose)

    phosphate

    purine or pyrimidine

      G,C,A,T

  nucleoside

    mono-, di-, tri-phosphodiester bond

oligonucleotide

polynucleotide

Watson-Crick model

    X-ray diffraction

    major and minor grooves

    right-handed double helix

    antiparallel

    hydrogen bonds, bases stacked

    ten bases per turn

    complementarity

        hydrophobic (inside)

        hydrophilic (outside)

A-DNA, B-DNA, Z-DNA (others also)

RNA

    rRNA, tRNA, mRNA

        primary transcript

        small nuclear RNA (snRNA)

        telomerase RNA

        antisense RNA

Svedberg coefficient (S)

Spectrophotometry

Processes/Methods

Replication (F10.1)

Storage of information (F10.1)

Expression (F10.1)

    transcription

    translation

Variation (mutation)(F10.1)

Transformation

    Diplococcus pneumoniae

        virulent (S)

        avirulent (R)

        serotypes (II, III)

        heat-killed IIIS

            protease

            ribonuclease

            deoxyribonuclease

    transfection

    recombinant DNA research

        insulin

        interferon

        human ß-globin gene

        transgenic mice

            growth hormone

    RNA as genetic material

        TMV (tobacco mosaic virus)

Qß phage

    Qß RNA replicase

  retroviruses

    reverse transcription

X-Ray diffraction

Hydrogen bonding

Semiconservative replication

Molecular Hybridization

  in situ

  FISH

  reassociation kinetics

  half reaction time (C_{ot})

  repetitive sequences

  unique (single copy) sequences

Electrophoresis

  size and rate of migration

Concepts

Information flow

Central dogma of molecular genetics

Evidence (direct and indirect) - DNA is genetic material

  transformation and transgenic animals

Differential labeling of macromolecules

Circumstantial evidence (DNA in eukaryotes)

  DNA distributions, ploidy

  mutagenesis

    action and absorption spectra

    260 nm, 280 nm

Recombinant DNA technology

  transgenic organisms

Molecular hybridization and sequence complexity

RNA as genetic material (some viruses)

F10.1. Illustration of relationships between DNA, its functions, and related products.

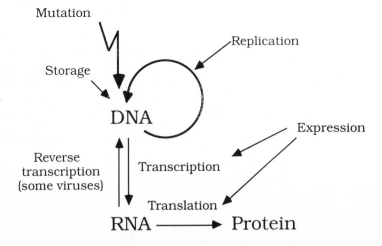

Solutions to Problems and
Discussion Questions

1. *Replication* is that process which leads to the production of identical copies of the existing genetic information. Since daughter cells contain essentially exact copies (with some exceptions) of genetic information of the parent cell, and through the production and union of gametes, offspring contain copies (with variation) of parental genetic information, the genetic material must make copies (replicate) of itself. Replication is accomplished during the S phase of interphase.

The genetic material is capable of *expression* through the production of a phenotype. Through transcription and translation, proteins are produced which contribute to the phenotype of the organism. The genetic material must be stable enough to maintain information in "*storage*" from one cell to the next and one organism to the next. Because the genetic material is not "used up" in the processes of transcription and translation, genetic information can be stored and used constantly.

Above, it was stated that the genetic material must be stable enough to store genetic information; however, variation through *mutation* provides the raw material for evolution. The genetic material is capable of a variety of changes, both at the chromosomal and nucleotide levels. See F10.1.

2. Prior to 1940, most of the interest in genetics centered on the transmission of similarity and variation from parents to offspring (transmission genetics). While some experiments examined the possible nature of the hereditary material, abundant knowledge of the structural and enzymatic properties of proteins generated a bias which worked to favor proteins as the hereditary substance. In addition, proteins were composed of as many as twenty different subunits (amino acids), thereby providing ample structural and functional variation for the multiple tasks which must be accomplished by the genetic material. The tetranucleotide hypothesis (structure) provided insufficient variability to account for the diverse roles of the genetic material.

3. Griffith performed experiments with different strains of *Diplococcus pneumoniae* in which a heat-killed pathogen, when injected into a mouse with a live non-pathogenic strain, eventually led to the mouse's death. A summary of this experiment is provided in *Essentials*. Examination of the dead mice revealed living pathogenic bacteria. Griffith suggested that the heat-killed virulent (pathogenic) bacteria transformed the avirulent (nonpathogenic) strain into a virulent strain.

Avery and co-workers systematically searched for the transforming principle originating from the heat-killed pathogenic strain and determined it to be DNA. Taylor showed that transformed bacteria are capable of serving as donors of transforming DNA, indicating that the process of transformation involves a stable alteration in the genetic material (DNA).

4. Nucleic acids contain large amounts of phosphorus and no sulfur, whereas proteins contain sulfur and no phosphorus. Therefore, the radioisotopes ^{32}P and ^{35}S will selectively label nucleic acids and proteins, respectively.

The Hershey and Chase experiment is based on the premise that the substance injected into the bacterium is the substance responsible for producing the progeny phage and therefore must be the hereditary material. The experiment demonstrated that most of the ^{32}P-labeled material (DNA) was injected while the phage ghosts (protein coats) remained outside the bacterium. Therefore, the nucleic acid must be the genetic material.

5. The early evidence would be considered circumstantial in that at no time was there an experiment, like transformation in bacteria, in which genetic information in one organism was transferred to another using DNA. Rather, by comparing DNA content in various cell types (sperm and somatic cells) and observing that the *action* and *absorption* spectra of ultraviolet light were correlated, DNA was considered to be the genetic material. This suggestion was supported by the fact that DNA was shown to be the genetic material in bacteria and some phage. Direct evidence for DNA being the genetic material comes from a variety of observations including gene transfer, which has been facilitated by recombinant DNA techniques.

6. Some viruses contain a genetic material composed of RNA. The tobacco mosaic virus is composed of an RNA core and a protein coat. "Crosses" can be made in which the protein coat and RNA of TMV are interchanged with another strain (Holmes ribgrass). The source of the RNA determines the type of lesion, thus, RNA is the genetic material in these viruses. Retroviruses contain RNA as the genetic material and use an enzyme known as *reverse transcriptase* to produce DNA, which can be integrated into the host chromosome. See F9.1.

7. The structure of deoxyadenylic acid is given below. Linkages among the three components require the removal of water (H_2O).

8. Examine the structures of the bases in the *Essentials* text. The other bases would be named as follows:

Guanine: 2-amino-6-oxypurine

Cytosine: 2-oxy-4-aminopyrimidine

Thymine: 2,4-dioxy-5-methylpyrimidine

Uracil: 2,4-dioxypyrimidine

9. The following are characteristics of the Watson-Crick double-helix model for DNA:

The base composition is such that A=T, G=C and (A+G) = (C+T). Bases are stacked, 0.34 nm apart, in a plectonic, antiparallel manner. There is one complete turn for each 3.4 nm, which constitutes 10 bases per turn. Hydrogen bonds hold the two polynucleotide chains together, each being formed by phosphodiester linkages between the sugars and the phosphates. There are two hydrogen bonds forming the A to T pair and three forming the G to C pair. The double helix exists as a twisted structure, approximately 20 nm in diameter, with a topography of major and minor grooves. The hydrophobic bases are located in the center of the molecule while the hydrophilic phosphodiester backbone is on the outside.

10. In addition to creative "genius" and perseverance, model building skills, and the conviction that the structure would turn out to be "simple" and have a natural beauty in its simplicity, Watson and Crick employed the X-ray diffraction information of Franklin and Wilkins, and the base ratio information of Chargaff.

11. Because in double-stranded DNA, A=T and G=C (within limits of experimental error), the data presented would have indicated a lack of pairing of these bases in favor of a single-stranded structure or some other nonhydrogen-bonded structure. Alternatively, from the data it would appear that A=G and T=C, which would require purines to pair with purines and pyrimidines to pair with pyrimidines. In that case, the DNA would have contradicted the data from Franklin and Watkins, which called for a constant diameter for the double-stranded structure.

12. Three main differences between RNA and DNA are the following:

(1) uracil in RNA replaces thymine in DNA,

(2) ribose in RNA replaces deoxyribose in DNA, and

(3) RNA often occurs as both single- and partially double-stranded forms, whereas DNA most often occurs in a double-stranded form.

13. The reassociation of separate complementary strands of a nucleic acid, either DNA or RNA, is based on hydrogen bonds forming between A-T (or U) and G-C.

14. In order for hydrogen bonds to form between complementary base pairs, complementary strands of nucleic acids must be in proximity. For a given concentration of nucleic acids, the more copies of a given type of nucleic acid that are present, the higher the likelihood that complementary strands will be close to each other. Conversely, unique sequences of nucleic acids have a lower probability of interacting because there are fewer of them; thus, the likelihood of forming hydrogen bonds (hybridizing) is less.

15.

(1) As shown, the extra phosphate is not normally expected.

(2) In the adenine ring, a nitrogen is at position 8 rather than position 9.

(3) The bond from the C'-1 to the sugar should form with the N at position 9 (N-9) of the adenine.

(4) The dinucleotide is a "deoxy" form, therefore each C-2' should not have a hydroxyl group. Notice the hydroxyl group at C'-2 on the sugar of the adenylic acid.

(5) At the C-5 position on the thymine residue, there should be a methyl group.

(6) At the C'-5 position on the thymidylic acid, there is an extra OH group.

16. Without knowing the exact bonding characteristics of hypoxanthine or xanthine, it may be difficult to predict the likelihood of each pairing type. It is likely that both are of the same class (purine or pyrimidine) because the names of the molecules indicate a similarity. In addition, the diameter of the structure is constant which, under the model to follow, would be expected. In fact, hypoxanthine and xanthine are both purines.

Because there are equal amounts of A, T and H, one could suggest that they are hydrogen bonded to each other; the same may be said for C, G, and X. Given the molar equivalence of erythrose and phosphate, an alternating sugar-phosphate-sugar backbone as in "earth-type" DNA would be acceptable. A model of a triple helix would be acceptable, since the diameter is constant. Given the chemical similarities to "earth-type" DNA it is probable that the unique creature's DNA follows the same structural plan.

17.

(i) The X-ray diffraction studies would indicate a helical structure, for it is on the basis of such data that a helical pattern is suggested. The fact that it is irregular may indicate different diameters (base pairings), additional strands in the helix, kinking or bending.

(ii) The hyperchromic shift would indicate considerable hydrogen bonding, possibly caused by base pairing.

(iii) Such data may suggest irregular base pairing in which purines bind purines (all the bases presented are purines), thus giving the atypical dimensions.

(iv) Because of the presence of ribose, the molecule may show more flexibility, kinking, and/or folding.

While there are several situations possible for this model, the phosphates are still likely to be far apart (on the outside) because of their strong like charges. Hydrogen bonding probably exists on the inside of the molecule and there is probably considerable flexibility, kinking, and/or bending.

18. Since cytosine pairs with guanine and uracil pairs with adenine, the result would be a base substitution of G:C to A:T after DNA replication.

19. Under this condition, the hydrolyzed 5-methyl cytosine becomes thymine.

20. Carefully examine the K/C text. First understand the concept of molecular hybridization, then see that as the degree of strand uniqueness increases, the time required for reassociation increases. Repetitive sequences renature relatively quickly because the likelihood of complementary strands interacting increases.

For curve *A* in the problem, there is evidence for a rapidly renaturing species (repetitive) and a slowly renaturing species (unique). The fraction which reassociates faster than the *E. coli* DNA is highly repetitive and the last fraction (with the highest $C_o t_{1/2}$ value) contains primarily unique sequences. Fraction *B* contains mostly unique, relatively complex DNA.

Chapter 11: DNA Replication and Synthesis

Concept Areas	Corresponding Problems
Replication	4, 6, 9, 10, 11, 12, 15, 16, 20
Models of Replication	1
Experimentation	2, 3, 5, 7
5' - 3' Polarity	8, 13
Recombination	14

Vocabulary and Critical Issues

Structures and Substances

DNA polymerase I, II, III

  holoenzyme

    dimer

  subunits

   polA1

5'-nucleotides (F11.1)

3'-nucleotides (F11.1)

Phage øX174

Helicase

Single-stranded DNA binding proteins
    (SSBPs)

DNA gyrase (a topoisomerase)

  replisome

RNA primer

  primase

   3' - free hydroxyl group

DNA ligase

  ligase deficient mutant

ori C

  ter

  9mer, 13mer

dnaA, dnaB, dnaC

DnaA.... proteins

β-subunit clamp

Core enzyme

  conditional mutations

    temperature sensitive

Autonomous Replicating Sequences (ARSs)

polα, δ. ε

Eukaryotic DNA

  nucleosome

  six kinds (polymerase)

  multireplicons

telomeres

    telomerase

    ribonucleoprotein (catalytic)

Recombination

  homologous (general)

Heteroduplex DNA molecules

  Holliday structure

  chi form

  recA (RecA protein)

  recB, recC, recD

Processes/Methods

Replication of DNA (models)

  semiconservative

    Meselson and Stahl - 1958

      E. coli

      equilibrium centrifugation

      ^{15}N, ^{14}N (in ammonium chloride)

    Taylor, Woods, and Hughes - 1957

      Vicia faba

        colchicine

      ^{3}H-thymidine

      autoradiography

        sister chromatid exchange

  conservative replication

  dispersive replication

  bidirectional (vs. unidirectional)

origin of replication, *ori*

replicon

    multiple origins (eukaryotic)

  replication fork, supercoiling

  continuous, discontinuous

    leading strand

    lagging strand

      Okazaki fragments

Synthesis of DNA *in vitro*

  reaction mixture

  biologically active DNA

  fidelity

Exonuclease activity

Proofreading and error correction

  3'-5' exonuclease activity

Eukaryotic DNA replicase

  polymerase switching

  processivity

Genetic recombination

  single-stranded nick

  endonuclease

  branch migration

Gene conversion

  Neurospora

  nonreciprocal

Concepts

Replication Models

  semiconservative

    complementarity

    antiparallel

    continuous, discontinuous

  conservative

dispersive

5' - 3' polarity restrictions

Supercoiling

Concurrent synthesis

Recombination

Gene conversion

Conditional mutants (F11.2)

F11.1 Shorthand structures for 3' and 5' nucleotides.

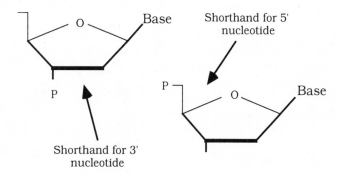

F11.2. Illustration of the influence of a conditional mutant on protein structure and therefore function.

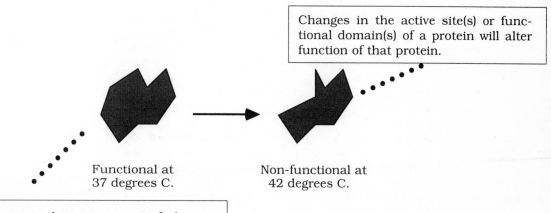

Changes in the active site(s) or functional domain(s) of a protein will alter function of that protein.

Functional at
37 degrees C.

Non-functional at
42 degrees C.

Changes in the environment of the protein may cause conformational changes in the protein.

Solutions to Problems and Discussion Questions

1. Refer to Question #1 of the *Insights and Solutions* section of Chapter 10 in *Essentials*. The differences among the three models of DNA replication relate to the manner in which the new strands of DNA are oriented as daughter DNA molecules are produced.

Conservative: In the conservative scheme, the original double helix remains as a complete unit and the new DNA double helix is produced as a single unit. The old DNA is completely *conserved*.

Semiconservative: Each daughter strand is composed of one old DNA strand and one new DNA strand. Separation of hydrogen bonds is required.

Dispersive: In the dispersive scheme, the original DNA strand is broken into pieces and the new DNA in the daughter strand is interspersed among the old pieces. Separation of covalent (phosphodiester) bonds is required for this mode of replication.

2. Under a conservative scheme, the first round of replication in ^{14}N medium produces one dense double helix and one "light" double helix in contrast to the intermediate density of the DNA in the semiconservative mode. Therefore, after one round or replication in the ^{14}N medium, the conservative scheme can be ruled out.

After one round of replication in ^{14}N under a dispersive model, the DNA is of intermediate density, just as it is in the semiconservative model. However, in the next round of replication in ^{14}N medium, the density of the DNA is between the intermediate and "light" densities. Refer to Question #1 of the *Insights and Solutions* section of Chapter 11 in *Essentials* if you have trouble answering this question.

3. Refer to the *Essentials* text for an illustration of the labeling of *Vicia* chromosomes under a Taylor, Woods, and Hughes experimental design. Notice that only those cells which pass through the S phase in the presence of the ^{3}H-thymidine are labeled and that each double helix (per chromatid) is "half-labeled."

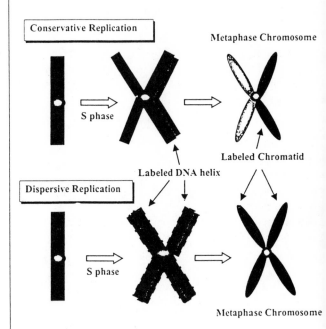

(a) Under a conservative scheme, all of the newly labeled DNA will go to one sister chromatid, while the other sister chromatid will remain unlabeled. In contrast to a semiconservative scheme, the first replicative round would produce one sister chromatid which has label on both strands of the double helix.

(b) Under a dispersive scheme all of the newly labeled DNA will be interspersed with unlabeled DNA. Because these preparations (metaphase chromosomes) are highly coiled and condensed structures derived from the "spread out" form at interphase (which includes the S phase) it is impossible to detect the areas where label is not found. Rather, both sister chromatids would appear as evenly labeled structures.

4. The *in vitro* replication requires a DNA template, a divalent cation (Mg⁺⁺), and all four of the deoxyribonucleoside triphosphates: dATP, dCTP, dTTP, and dGTP. The lower case "d" refers to the deoxyribose sugar.

5. As stated in the text, *biologically active* DNA implies that the DNA is capable of supporting typical metabolic activities of the cell or organism and is capable of faithful reproduction.

6. øX174 is a well-studied, single-stranded virus (phage) which can be easily isolated. It has a relatively small DNA genome (5500 nucleotides) which, if mutated, usually alters its reproductive cycle.

7. The *polAI* mutation was instrumental in demonstrating that DNA polymerase I activity was not necessary for the *in vivo* replication of the *E. coli* chromosome. Such an observation opened the door for the discovery of other enzymes involved in DNA replication.

8. All three enzymes share several common properties. First, none can *initiate* DNA synthesis on a template but all can *elongate* an existing DNA strand, assuming there is a template strand as shown in the figure below. Polymerization of nucleotides occurs in the 5' to 3' direction where each 5' phosphate is added to the 3' end of the growing polynucleotide. All three enzymes are large complex proteins with a molecular weight in excess of 100,000 daltons and each has 3' to 5' exonuclease activity. Refer to *Essentials* for a listing of enzyme properties.

DNA polymerase I:
  5' to 3' polymerization
  3' to 5' exonuclease activity
  5' to 3' exonuclease activity
  present in large amounts
  relatively stable

DNA polymerase II:
  5' to 3' polymerization
  3' to 5' exonuclease activity

DNA polymerase III:
  5' to 3' polymerization
  3' to 5' exonuclease activity
  essential for replication
  complex molecule
      ten polypeptide chains

9. *Helicase, dnaA* and *single-stranded DNA binding* proteins initially unwind, open, and stabilize DNA at the initiation point. *DNA gyrase*, a DNA topoisomerase, relieves supercoiling generated by helix unwinding. This process involves breaking both strands of the DNA helix.

10. *Okazaki fragments* are relatively short (1000 to 2000 bases in prokaryotes) DNA fragments which are synthesized in a discontinuous fashion on the lagging strand during DNA replication. Such fragments appear to be necessary because template DNA is not available for 5' > 3' synthesis until some degree of continuous DNA synthesis occurs on the leading strand in the direction of the replication fork. The isolation of such fragments provides support for the scheme of replication shown in the *Essentials* text.

DNA ligase is required to form phosphodiester linkages in gaps which are generated when DNA polymerase I removes RNA primer and meets newly synthesized DNA ahead of it.

Notice in the *Essentials* text, the discontinuous DNA strands are ligated together into a single continuous strand.

Synthesis of DNA
can be initiated here

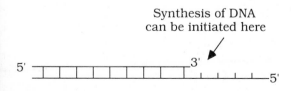

Primer RNA is formed by RNA primase to serve as an initiation point for the production of DNA strands on a DNA template. None of the DNA polymerases are capable of initiating synthesis without a free 3' hydroxyl group. The primer RNA provides that group and thus can be used by DNA polymerase III.

11. The synthesis of DNA is thought to follow the pattern described in the *Essentials* text. The model involves opening and stabilizing the DNA helix, priming DNA with synthesis with RNA primer, movement of replication forks in both directions which includes elongation of RNA primers in continuous and discontinuous 5' > 3' modes after removal of the RNA primer. Okazaki fragments generated in the replicative process are joined together with DNA ligase. DNA gyrase relieves supercoils generated by DNA unwinding.

12. Eukaryotic DNA is replicated in a manner which is very similar to that of *E. coli*. Synthesis is bidirectional, continuous on one strand and discontinuous on the other, and the requirements of synthesis (four deoxyribonucleoside triphosphates, divalent cation, template, and primer) are the same. Okazaki fragments of eukaryotes are about one-tenth the size of those in bacteria.

Because there is a much greater amount of DNA to be replicated and DNA replication is slower, there are multiple initiation sites for replication in eukaryotes and increased abouts of DNA po;ymerase in contrast to the single replication origin in prokaryotes. Replication occurs at different sites during different intervals of the S phase. The proposed functions of four DNA polymerases are described in the text.

13. In eukaryotes, the "ends" of chromosomes present a problem in that the 3' end of the lagging strand is an inadequate template, thus, a gap is possible without a unique enzyme called *telomerase*. In some organisms, special telomeric sequences of DNA allow the telomerase to complete replication. The *Tetrahymena* telomerase is known to contain a short piece of RNA which is complementary to the sequence whose synthesis it directs.

14. *Gene conversion* is likely to be a consequence of genetic recombination in which nonreciprocal recombination yields products in which it appears that one allele is "converted" to another. Gene conversion is now considered a result of heteroduplex formation which is accompanied by mismatched bases. When these mismatches are corrected, the "conversion" occurs.

15. (a) Because DNA polymerase III is essential for DNA chain elongation, it is necessary for replication of the *E. coli* chromosome. Thus, strains which are mutant for this enzyme must contain conditional mutations. **(b)** The 3' - 5' exonuclease activity is involved in proofreading. Thus, proofreading would be hampered in such mutant strains and a higher than expected mutation rate would occur.

16. (a) In *E. coli*, 100kb are added to each growing chain per minute. Therefore, the chain should be about 4,000,000bp.

(b) Given $(4 \times 10^6 \text{ bp}) \times 0.34 \text{nm/bp} =$

$$1.36 \times 10^6 \text{nm or } 1.3 \text{mm}$$

17. Since synthesis is bidirectional, one can multiply the rate of synthesis by two to come up with a figure of 18,000 bases replicated per five minutes (30bases/second X 300 seconds). Dividing 1.6×10^8 by 1.8×10^4 gives 0.88×10^4 or about 8,800 replication sites.

Chapter 12: The Genetic Code and Transcription

Concept Areas	Corresponding Problems
Genetic Code	1, 5, 9, 10
Deciphering the Code	2, 3, 4, 5,7, 8
Characteristics of the Code	6, 11, 16
Transcription	12, 13, 14, 15, 16, 17
Mutation	18

Vocabulary and Critical Issues

Structures and Substances

Codon

  triplet

Messenger RNA

Polynucleotide phosphorylase

  random proportional assembly of nucleotides

Homopolymer codes

  RNA homopolymers

  RNA heteropolymers

   anticodon

Ribosome

RNA polymerase

  holoenzyme

  (α, β, β', σ)

  consensus sequences

   template and partner strands

Pribnow box (-10) TATA

-35 region

termination factor (rho)

Messenger RNA (mRNA)

  polycistronic mRNA

  monocistronic mRNA

RNA polymerase (eukaryotic) - I, II, III

  heterogeneous nuclear RNA (hnRNA)

  heterogeneous nuclear ribonucleoprotein (hnRNP)

  nucleoside triphosphates (NTPs)

  nucleoside monophosphates (NMPs)

  nucleotides

  promoters (promoter sequences)

Consensus sequences

  adenine and thymine richness

  cis-acting elements

Goldberg-Hogness (-30, TATA box)

CAAT sequence

enhancers

trans-acting factors

transcription factors

TATA-factor (TFIIA, B, D)

TATA-binding protein (TBP)

pre-mRNAs

poly-A

cap (7mG)

    5' to 5'

split genes (intervening sequences)

    introns

    exons

    heteroduplexes

β-globin gene

ovalbumin gene

dystrophin

Processes/Methods

Transcription, Translation (F12.1)

Frameshifts

Cell-free protein-synthesizing system

    ribosomes, tRNAs, amino acids, etc.

    artificial mRNAs

Triplet binding assay

Transcription

(mRNA, evidence for)

    template binding

    denaturation (unwinding)

    initiation

    chain elongation (5' to 3')

    chain termination

    gene amplification

RNA processing

    split genes

    post-transcriptional changes

        poly-A (3'), cap (5')

    mechanisms

        rRNA self-excision (ribozyme)

        spliceosome

            snRNAs, snurps (snRNP)

        branch point

        alternative splicing

        isoforms

RNA editing

    substitution

    insertion/deletion

    guide RNA (gRNA)

Concepts

Genetic code

    linear

    triplet codon

frameshift mutations (r_{II})

(+++)(- - -)

codon assignments

artificial mRNAs

triplet binding assay

repeating copolymers

unambiguous

degenerate, wobble

support for degenerate code

punctuation

start (initiation), AUG, GUG (rare)

stop (termination), UAA, UAG, UGA

nonoverlapping

support for nonoverlapping code

universal, exceptions

ordered codon assignments

Hypotheses

adaptor molecule

messenger RNA

wobble hypothesis

pattern of degeneracy

Information flow (F12.2)

transcription

gene amplification

RNA splicing

Alternative splicing, RNA editing

Comparisons (eukaryotic, prokaryotic)

F12.1 Polarity constraints associated with simultaneous transcription and translation (see chapter 14). The RNA polymerase is moving downward (bold arrow) in this drawing.

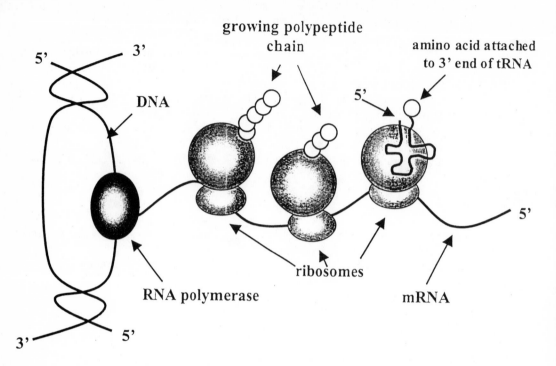

F12.2. Illustration of the processes, transcription and translation, involved in protein synthesis. Such relationships are often called the **Central Dogma**.

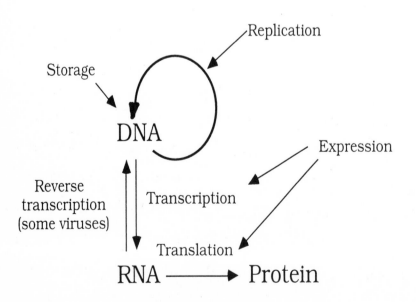

Solutions to Problems
and Discussion Questions

1. No. The term "reading frame" refers to the number of bases contained in each codon. The reason that (+++) or (- - -) restored the reading frame *is because* the code is triplet. By having the (+++) or (- - -), the translation system is "out of phase" until the third "+" or "-" is encountered. If the code contained six nucleotides (a sextuplet code), then the translation system is "out of phase" until the sixth "+" or "-" is encountered.

2. (a) The way to determine the fraction which each triplet will occur with a random incorporation system is to determine the likelihood that each base will occur in each position of the codon (first, second, third), then multiply the individual probabilities (fractions) for a final probability (fraction).

GGG $= 3/4 \times 3/4 \times 3/4 = 27/64$

GGC $= 3/4 \times 3/4 \times 1/4 = 9/64$

GCG $= 3/4 \times 1/4 \times 3/4 = 9/64$

CGG $= 1/4 \times 3/4 \times 3/4 = 9/64$

CCG $= 1/4 \times 1/4 \times 3/4 = 3/64$

CGC $= 1/4 \times 3/4 \times 1/4 = 3/64$

GCC $= 3/4 \times 1/4 \times 1/4 = 3/64$

CCC $= 1/4 \times 1/4 \times 1/4 = 1/64$

(b) Glycine:

GGG and one G_2C (adds up to 36/64)

Alanine:

one G_2C and one C_2G (adds up to 12/64)

Arginine:
one G_2C and one C_2G (adds up to 12/64)

Proline:

one C_2G and CCC (adds up to 4/64)

(c) With the wobble hypothesis, variation can occur in the third position of each codon.

Glycine: GGG, GGC

Alanine: CGG, GCC, CGC, GCG

Arginine: GCG, GCC, CGC, CGG

Proline: CCC, CCG

3. First, compute the frequency (percentages would be easiest to compare) for each of the random codons.

For 4/5 C: 1/5 A:

CCC $= 4/5 \times 4/5 \times 4/5 = 64/125$ (51.2%)

$C_2A = 3(4/5 \times 4/5 \times 1/5) = 48/125$ (38.4%)

$CA_2 = 3(4/5 \times 1/5 \times 1/5) = 12/125$ (9.6%)

AAA $= 1/5 \times 1/5 \times 1/5 = 1/125$ (0.8%)

For 4/5 A: 1/5 C:

AAA $= 4/5 \times 4/5 \times 4/5 = 64/125$ (51.2%)

$A_2C = 3(4/5 \times 4/5 \times 1/5) = 48/125$ (38.4%)

$AC_2 = 3(4/5 \times 1/5 \times 1/5) = 12/125$ (9.6%)

CCC $= 1/5 \times 1/5 \times 1/5 = 1/125$ (0.8%)

Proline:	C_3, and one of the C_2A triplets
Histidine:	one of the C_2A triplets
Threonine:	one C_2A triplet, and one A_2C triplet
Glutamine:	one of the A_2C triplets
Asparagine:	one of the A_2C triplets
Lysine:	A_3

4. As in the previous problem the procedure is to find those sequences which are the same for the first two bases but which vary in the third base. Given that AGG = arg, then information from the AG copolymer indicates that AGA also codes for arg and GAG must therefore code for glu. Coupling this information with that of the AAG copolymer, GAA must also code for glu, and AAG must code for lys.

5. The basis of the technique is that if a trinucleotide contains bases (a codon) which are complementary to the anticodon of a charged tRNA, a relatively large complex is formed which contains the ribosome, the tRNA, and the trinucleotide. This complex is trapped in the filter whereas the components by themselves are not trapped. If the amino acid on a charged, trapped tRNA is radioactive, then the filter becomes radioactive.

6. Apply the most conservative pathway of change.

```
                        thr (ACA)
             arg ──────  ser  (AGU,C)
            (AGA)        ile (AUA)
  gly  ────
 (GGA)
             glu ──────  val (GUA)
            (GAA)        ala (GCA)
```

7. The enzyme generally functions in the degradation of RNA, however in an *in vitro* environment, with high concentrations of the ribonucleoside diphosphates, the direction of the reaction can be forced toward polymerization. *In vivo*, the concentration of ribonucleoside diphosphates is low and the degradative process is favored.

8. Because Poly U is complementary to Poly A, double-stranded structures will be formed. In order for an RNA to serve as a messenger RNA it must be single-stranded thereby exposing the bases for interaction with ribosomal subunits and tRNAs.

9. Applying the coding dictionary, the following sequences are "decoded"

Sequence 1:   met-pro-asp-tyr-ser-(term)
Sequence 2:   met-pro-asp-(term)

The 12th base (a uracil) is deleted from Sequence #1 thereby causing a frameshift mutation.

10. Given the sequence GGA, by changing each of the bases to the remaining three bases, then checking the code table, one can determine whether amino acid substitutions will occur.

G G A > gly	G G U > gly
U G A > **term**	G G C > gly
C G A > **arg**	G G A > gly
A G A > **arg**	G G G > gly
G U A > **val**	U G U > **cys**
G C A > **ala**	C G U > **arg**
G A A > **glu**	A G U > **ser**
G G U > gly	G U U > **val**
G G C > gly	G C U > **ala**
G G A > gly	G A U > **asp**

11. By examining the coding dictionary one will notice that the number of codons for each particular amino acid (synonyms) is directly related to the frequency of amino acid incorporation stated in the problem.

12. The central dogma of molecular genetics and to some, all of biology, states that DNA produces, through transcription, RNA, which is "decoded" (during translation) to produce proteins. See F12.2 for a graphic description.

13. Several observations indicated that a "messenger" molecule exists. First, DNA, the genetic material, is located in the nucleus of a eukaryotic cell whereas protein synthesis occurs in the cytoplasm. DNA, therefore, does not directly participate in protein synthesis. Second, RNA, which is chemically similar to DNA is synthesized in the nucleus of eukaryotic cells. Much of the RNA migrates to the cytoplasm, the site of protein synthesis. Third, there is generally a direct correlation between the amounts of RNA and protein in a cell. More direct support was derived from experiments showing that an RNA other than that found in ribosomes was involved in protein synthesis and shortly after phage infection, an RNA species is produced which is complementary to phage DNA.

14. RNA polymerase from *E. coli* is a complex, large (almost 500,000 daltons) molecule composed of subunits (α, β, β', σ) in the proportion $\alpha2$, β, β', σ for the holoenzyme. The β subunit provides catalytic function while the sigma (σ) subunit is involved in recognition of specific promoters. The core enzyme is the protein without the sigma subunit.

15. Ribonucleoside triphosphates and a DNA template in the presence of RNA polymerase and a divalent cation (Mg^{++}) produce a ribonucleoside monophosphate polymer, DNA, and pyrophosphate (diphosphate). Equimolar amounts of precursor ribonucleoside triphosphates, and product ribonucleoside monophosphates and pyrophosphates (diphosphates) are formed. In *E. coli* transcription and translation can occur simultaneously. Ribosomes add to the 5' end of nascent mRNA and progress to the 3' end during translation. While transcription/translation can be "visualized" in *E. coli* (F12.1), the predominant components "visualized" are the strings of ribosomes (polysomes).

16. Apply complementary bases, substituting U for T: (Note: some printings of the text may have a UAC to start, this should be TAC)

(a)

Sequence 1: GAAAAAACGGUA

Sequence 2: UGUAGUUAUUGA

Sequence 3: AUGUUCCCAAGA

(b)

Sequence 1: *glu-lys-thr-val*

Sequence 2: *cys-ser-tyr*

Sequence 3: *met-phe-pro-arg*

(c) Because there are no punctuation codons in Sequence 1, it must be in the middle. Sequence 2, having a termination codon (UGA), must be in the terminal portion. Sequence 3, with the AUG starting codon, must be in the initial portion.

17.

(a) #1: *nonsense mutation*
#2: *missense mutation*
#3: *frameshift mutation*

(b) #1: mutation in third position to A or G
#2: change from U to C in third triplet
#3: removal of a G in the UGG triplet (trp)

(c) termination

(d) All of the amino acids can be assigned specific triplets including the third base of each triplet. Compare the sequences for the wild type and mutant #2. After removal of a G in the UGG triplet of tryptophan, the frameshift mutation shifts the first base of the following triplet to the third (often ambiguous) base of the previous triplet. The only tricky solution is with serine which has six triplet possibilities, but it can stil be resolved.

AUG UGG UAU CGU GGU AGU CCA ACA

(e) The mutation may be in a promoter or enhancer, although many posttranscriptional alterations are possible. Depending on the gene and the organism, the mutation may be in an intron/exon splice site, *etc.*

Chapter 13: Translation and Proteins

Concept Areas

Translation
RNAs
Information Flow
One-gene: One-enzyme
Pathways
Proteins
Mutation

Corresponding Problems

1, 4, 24
2, 3, 6, 7
5
8, 9, 10, 14
11, 12, 13, 25
15, 16, 17, 18, 19, 20, 21, 22
23

Vocabulary and Critical Issues

Structures and Substances

Polypeptide, protein

Amino acid

  carboxyl group

  amino group

  R (radical) group

  central carbon

  nonpolar (hydrophobic)

  polar (hydrophilic)

    negative, positive

Peptide bond

  dipeptide, tripeptide

  N-terminus, C-terminus

Primary structure

Secondary structure

  α-helix, β-pleated sheet

  fibroin

Tertiary structure

  hemoglobin

  myoglobin

Oligimer

Protomer (subunit)

Kinase

  glycoproteins

  signal sequence

  protein targeting

Chaperone

Ribosome

  monosome (70S, 80S)

rRNA

rDNA

  5S, 16S, 23S RNA (single transcript)

  5.8S, 18S, 28S RNA (single transcript)

  tendem repeats and spacer DNA

subunits

ribosomal proteins

Ribosome complex

    peptidyl (P site)

    aminoacyl (A site)

    exit (E site)

    GTP

    tunnel

    peptidyl transferase

Transfer RNAs - tRNA

    anticodon

    unusual bases

    cloverleaf model

        anticodon loop, codon

        ...pCpCpA (3')

        ...pG (5')

    aminoacyl tRNA synthetases

        charging

        activated form

            (aminoacyladenylic acid)

        isoaccepting tRNAs

Initiation factors

    initiation complex

    Shine-Delgarno sequence

Formylmethionine (N-formylmethionine)

    tRNA^{fmet}

Elongation factors

GTP-dependent release factors

    termination (nonsense)

    stop codon UAA, UAG, UGA

Polyribosomes (polysomes)

Heterogeneous RNA (hnRNA)

    poly-A

    cap (7mG)

    5' to 5'

    Kozak sequences

    5'-ACCAUGG

    Sec61

Inborn Errors of Metabolism

    alkaptonuria

        homogentisic acid

            2,5-dihydroxyphenylacetic acid

    phenylketonuria

        phenylalanine hydroxylase

    citrulline

    ornithine

    sickle-cell anemia (trait)

        HbA, HbS

        heme group

        globin portion

tryptophan synthetase

collagen

keratin

actin, myosin

immunoglobin

transport proteins

enzyme (active site)

hormone, receptor

anabolic, catabolic

protein domain

LDL receptor protein

Processes/Methods

Transcription, Translation

RNA processing

post-transcriptional modification

Translation

codon, anticodon

tRNA charging

aminoacyl tRNA synthetases

chain initiation

chain elongation

translocation

chain termination, UAG, UAA, UGA

Simultaneous transcription and translation (Prokaryotes, F12.1)

Starch gel electrophoresis

Fingerprinting technique

Colinear relationships

Exon shuffling

Endocytosis

Posttranslational modification

modification

trimming

complex formation

Concepts

Information flow

transcription

translation

Ribosome comparative morphology

Comparisons (eukaryotic, prokaryotic)

One-gene: one-enzyme hypothesis

One-gene: one protein

One-gene: one polypeptide chain

Pathway analysis

Colinearity

Protein Structure

Posttranslational modification

Structure/function relationships

Chapter 13

Solutions to Problems and Discussion Questions

1. A functional polyribosome will contain the following components: mRNA, charged tRNA, large and small ribosomal subunits, elongation and perhaps initiation factors, peptidyl transferase, GTP, Mg^{++}, nascent proteins, possibly GTP-dependent release factors.

2. Transfer RNAs are "adaptor" molecules in that they provide a way for amino acids to interact with sequences of bases in nucleic acids. Amino acids are specifically and individually attached to the 3' end of tRNAs which possess a three-base sequence (the anticodon) to base-pair with three bases of mRNA. Messenger RNA, on the other hand, contains a copy of the triplet codes which are stored in DNA. The sequences of bases in mRNA interact, three at a time, with the anti-codons of tRNAs.

Enzymes involved in transcription include the following: RNA polymerase (*E. coli*), and RNA polymerase I, II, III (eukaryotes). Those involved in translation include the following: aminoacyl tRNA synthetases, peptidyl transferase, and GTP-dependent release factors.

3. It was reasoned that there would not be sufficient affinity between amino acids and nucleic acids to account for protein synthesis. For example, acidic amino acids would not be attracted to nucleic acids. With an adaptor molecule, specific hydrogen bonding could occur between nucleic acids, and specific covalent bonding could occur between an amino acid and a nucleic acid tRNA.

4. The sequence of base triplets in mRNA constitutes the sequence of codons. A three-base portion of the tRNA constitutes the anticodon.

5. Since there are three nucleotides which code for each amino acid, there would be 423 code letters (nucleotides), 426 including a termination codon. This assumes that other features, such as the polyA tail, the 5'cap, and non-coding leader sequences are omitted. Dividing 20 by 0.34, gives the number of nucleotides (about 59) occupied by a ribosome. Dividing 59 by three gives the approximate number of triplet codes: approximately 20.

6. The steps involved in tRNA charging are outlined in the *Essentials* text. An amino acid in the presence of ATP, Mg^{++}, and a specific aminoacyl synthetase produces an amino acid-AMP enzyme complex (+ PP$_i$). This complex interacts with a specific tRNA to produce the aminoacyl tRNA.

7. The four sites in tRNA which provide for specific recognition are the following: attachment of the specific amino acid, interaction with the aminoacyl tRNA synthetase, interaction with the ribosome, and interaction with the codon (anticodon).

8. Phenylalanine is an amino acid which, like other amino acids, is required for protein synthesis. While too much phenylalanine and its derivatives cause PKU in phenylketonurics, too little will restrict protein synthesis.

9. Both phenylalanine and tyrosine can be obtained from the diet. Even though individuals with PKU can not convert phenylalanine to tyrosine, it is obtained from the diet.

10. Tyrosine is a precursor to melanin, skin pigment. Individuals with PKU fail to convert phenylalanine to tyrosine and even though tyrosine is obtained from the diet, at the population level, individuals with PKU have a tendency for less skin pigmentation.

11. (a) In this cross, two gene pairs are operating because the F_2 ratio is a modification of a 9:3:3:1 ratio, which is typical of a dihybrid cross. If one assumes that homozygosity for either or both of the two loci gives white, then let strain *A* be, *aaBB* and strain *B*, *AAbb*. The F_1 is *AaBb* and pigmented (purple). The typical F_2 ratio would be as follows:

9/16	*A_B_*	Purple
3/16	*aaB_*	white
3/16	*A_bb*	white
1/16	*aabb*	white

If a pathway exists which has the following structure, then the genetic and biochemical data are explained.

```
     aa         bb
      \          \
X ----\----> Y ----\---> Purple
(white)    (white)      pigment
```

(b) For this condition, with the pink phenotype present, leave the symbols the same, however, change the Y compound such that when accumulated, a pink phenotype is produced:

```
     aa         bb
      \          \
X -----\--> Y -----\---> Purple
(white)   (pink)       pigment
```

9/16	*A_B_*	Purple
3/16	*aaB_*	white
3/16	*A_bb*	**pink**
1/16	*aabb*	white

12. The best way to approach these types of problems, especially when the data are organized in the form given, is to realize that the substance (supplement) which "repairs" a strain, as indicated by a (+), is *after* the metabolic block for that strain. In addition, and most important, is that the substance which "repairs" the highest number of strains either *is the end product* or is *closest to the end* product.

Looking at the table, notice that the supplement tryptophan "repairs" all the strains. Therefore it must be at the end of the pathway or at least after all the metabolic blocks (defined by each mutation). Indole "repairs" the next highest number of strains (3) therefore it must be second from the end. Indole glycerol phosphate "repairs" two of the four strains so it is third from the end. Anthranilic acid "repairs" the least number of strains, so it must be early (first) in the pathway.

Minimal medium is void of supplements and mutant strains involving this pathway would not be expected to grow (or be "repaired"). The pathway therefore would be as follows:

```
AA----->IGP----->I----->TRY
```

To assign the various mutations to the pathway, keep in mind that if a supplement "repairs" a given mutant, the supplement must be after the metabolic block. Applying this rationale to the above pathway, the metabolic blocks are created at the following locations. (X = precursor to AA)

```
   trp-8    trp-2    trp-3    trp-1
      \        \        \        /
X---\->AA---\->IGP--\-->I--/--->TRY
```

13. In general the rationale for working with a branched chain pathway is similar to that stated in the previous problem. Since thiamine "repairs" each of the mutant strains, it must, as stated in the problem, be the final synthetic product.

Remembering the "one-gene:one-enzyme" statement, each metabolic block should only occur in one place, so even though pyrimidine and thiazole supplements each "repair" only one strain each, they will not occupy the same step; rather a branched pathway is suggested. Consider that pyrimidine and thiazole are products of distinct pathways and that both are needed to produce the end product, thiamine, as indicated below:

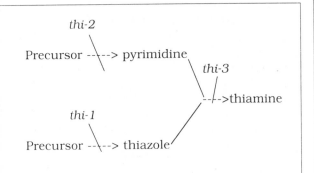

14. The fact that enzymes are a subclass of the general term *protein*, a *one-gene:one-protein* statement might seem to be more appropriate. However, some proteins are made up of subunits, each different type of subunit (polypeptide chain) being under the control of a different gene. Under this circumstance, the *one-gene:one-polypeptide* might be more reasonable.

It turns out that many functions of cells and organisms are controlled by stretches of DNA which either produce no protein product (operator and promoter regions, for example) or have more than one function as in the case of overlapping genes and differential mRNA splicing. A simple statement regarding the relationship of a stretch of DNA to its physical product is difficult to formulate.

15. The electrophoretic mobility of a protein is based on a variety of factors, primarily the net charge of the protein and to some extent, the conformation in the electrophoretic environment. Both are based on the type and sequence (primary structure) of the component amino acids of a protein.

The interactions (hydrogen bonds) of the components of the peptide bonds, hydrophobic, hydrophilic, and covalent interactions (as well as others) are all dependent on the original sequence of amino acids and take part in determining the final conformation of a protein. A change in the electrophoretic mobility of a protein would therefore indicate that the amino acid sequence had been changed.

16. Sickle-cell anemia is coined a *molecular* disease because it is well understood at the molecular level; at the level of a base change in DNA which leads to an amino acid change in the β chain of hemoglobin. It is a *genetic* disease in that it is inherited from one generation to the next. It is not contagious as might be the case of a disease caused by a microorganism. Diseases caused by microorganisms may not necessarily follow family blood lines whereas genetic diseases do.

17. In the late 1940's Pauling demonstrated a difference in the electrophoretic mobility of HbA and HbS (sickle-cell hemoglobin) and concluded that the difference had a chemical basis. Ingram determined that the chemical change occurs in the primary structure of the globin portion of the molecule using the fingerprinting technique. He found a change in the 6th amino acid in the β chain.

18. It is possible for an amino acid to change without changing the electrophoretic mobility of a protein under standard conditions. If the amino acid is substituted with an amino acid of like charge and similar structure there is a chance that factors which influence electrophoretic mobility (primarily net charge) will not be altered. Other techniques such as chromatography of digested peptides may detect subtle amino acid differences.

19. *Colinearity* refers to the sequential arrangement of subunits, amino acids and nitrogenous bases in proteins and DNA, respectively. Sequencing of genes and products in MS2 phage and studies on mutations in the *A* subunit of the *tryptophan synthetase* gene indicate a colinear relationship.

20. As stated in the text, the four levels of protein structure are the following:

Primary: the linear sequence of amino acids. This sequence determines the higher level structures.

Secondary: α–helix and β-pleated-sheet structures generated by hydrogen bonds between components of the peptide bond.

Tertiary: folding which occurs as a result of interactions of the amino acid side chains. These interactions include, but are not limited to the following: covalent disulfide bonds between cysteine residues; interactions of hydrophilic side chains with water; interactions of hydrophobic side chains with each other.

Quaternary: the association of two (dimer) or more polypeptide chains. Called *oligomeric,* such a protein is made up of more than one *promoter.*

21. There are probably as many different types of proteins as there are different types of structures and functions in living systems. Your text lists the following:

Oxygen transport: hemoglobin, myoglobin
Structural: collagen, keratin, histones
Contractile: actin, myosin
Immune system: immunoglobins
Cross-membrane transport: a variety of proteins in and around membranes, such as receptor proteins.
Regulatory: hormones, perhaps histones
Catalytic: enzymes

22. Enzymes function to regulate catabolic and anabolic activities of cells. They influence (lower) the *energy of activation* thus allowing chemical reactions to occur under conditions which are compatible with living systems. Enzymes possess *active sites* and/or other domains which are sensitive to the environment. The active site is considered to be a crevice, or pit, which binds reactants, thus enhancing their interaction. The other domains mentioned above may influence the conformation and therefore function of the active site.

23. All of the substitutions involve one base change.

24. One can conclude that the amino acid is not involved in recognition of the codon.

25. A cross of the following nature would satisfy the data:

$$AABBCC \ X \ aabbcc$$

Offspring in the F2:

$$27 \ A\_B\_C\_ \ = \ purple$$

$$9 \ A\_B\_cc \ = \ pink$$

$$9 \ A\_bbC\_ \ = \ rose$$

$$9 \ aaB\_C\_ \ = \ orange$$

$$3 \ A\_bbcc \ = \ pink$$

$$3 \ aaB\_cc \ = \ pink$$

$$3 \ aabbC\_ \ = \ rose$$

$$1 \ aabbcc \ = \ pink$$

$$\overset{c}{pink-/->} \ \overset{b}{rose \ -/->} \ \overset{a}{orange \ -|-> purple}$$

The above hypothesis could be tested by conducting a backcross as given below:

$$AaBbCc \ X \ aabbcc$$

The cross should give a

4(pink):2(rose):1(orange):1(purple) ratio

Chapter 14: Gene Mutation, DNA Repair, and Transposable Elements

Concept Areas	Corresponding Problems
Chromosomal Aberrations	1
Gene Mutations	2, 3, 5, 6, 8, 14, 15
Rates	10, 13
Repair	7
Detection of Mutations	4, 12
Complementation	9
Transposable Elements	11

Vocabulary and Critical Issues

Structures and Substances

Somatic cells

Gametic cells

  germ line

  dominant/recessive

  autosomal/sex-linked

    hemophilia

5-Bromouracil

2-Amino purine

Acridine orange, proflavin

Mustard gas

Ethylmethane sulfonate

6-ethyl guanine

Electromagnetic spectrum

UV radiation

  pyrimidine dimers

ABO antigens

  H substance

    glycosyltransferase

Dystrophin

Pyrimidine dimers

uvr gene product

DNA polymerase I

DNA ligase

mutH, L, S and *U*

recA, lexA

Photoreactivation enzyme

Heterokaryon

Knockout mouse

Transgenic

Transposable elements

  insertion sequences (IS)

Inverted terminal repeat (ITR)

Ds (Dissociation)

Ac (Activator)

transposon (Tn) elements

controlling element

open reading frame (ORF)

transposase

copia

terminal repeats (DTR, ITR)

    P elements

Alu family

SINE

LINE

Processes/Methods

Variation by mutation

    chromosomal aberrations

    gene mutations

    spontaneous

        DNA replication

        background radiation

        rates

    induced

        cosmic sources

        mineral sources

        ultraviolet light

Molecular basis

    base substitution or point mutations

    missense

        transition

        transversion

        frameshift

    tautomeric shifts (forms)

        keto, enol

    base analogues

        5-bromouracil

        2-amino purine

    reverse mutation

    alkylation

    frameshift mutations

    apurinic sites

    deamination

Detection

    bacteria and fungi

        minimal medium

        complete medium

        prototrophs

        auxotrophs

    Drosophila

        attached-X procedure

plants

    biochemical

    visual observation

    tissue culture

humans

    electrophoresis

    DNA sequencing

        H substance modification

    muscular dystrophy

fragile-X

myotonic dystrophy

Huntington Disease

    trinucleotide DNA repeats

spinobulbar muscular atrophy
(Kennedy disease)

Ames test

    Salmonella typhimurium

    liver extract

    ultraviolet radiation (260nm)

        intensity of dose

            roentgen

            target theory

        pyrimidine dimers

        T-T, C-C, T-C

Repair

    photoreactivation

        photoreactivation enzyme (PRE)

excision repair

    base excision repair (BER)

    AP endonuclease

    uvr gene product

    DNA polymerase I

    DNA ligase

    AP site, AP endonuclease

        DNA glycosylase

    nucleotide excision repair (NER)

proofreading and mismatch repair

    DNA polymerase III

    strand discrimination

        DNA methylation

        adenine methylase

        mutH, L, S and *U*

    post-replication repair

recombinational repair

    recA, lexA, uvr

    SOS response

    xeroderma pigmentosum (XP)

        unscheduled DNA synthesis

        somatic cell hybridization

        heterokaryon

        somatic cell genetics

        complementation

Chapter 14

DNA double-stranded break repair (DSB)

homologous recombinational repair

Site-directed mutagenesis

Knockout genes (knockout organisms)

Transgenes (transgenetic organisms)

Genetic transposition

Hybrid dysgenesis

Concepts

Mutation - basis of organismic diversity (F14.1)

chromosomal aberrations

gene mutations

somatic (F14.2)

germ line (F14.2)

dominant autosomal

X-linked recessive

autosomal recessive

morphological

nutritional or biochemical

behavioral

regulatory

lethal

conditional

temperature-sensitive

trinucleotide repeats

repeat instability

Detection of mutations

Genetic anticipation

Mutation repair mechanisms

Complementation

Site-directed mutagenesis

Knockouts

Transposition

Genetic burden (load)

Hybrid dysgenesis

F14.1. Graphic representation of the relationship of mutation to Darwinian evolutionary theory. Mutation provides the original source of variation on which natural selection operates.

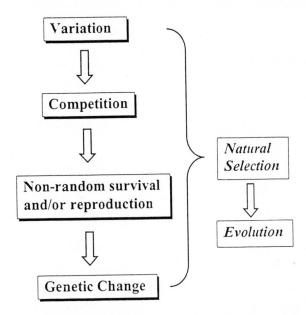

F14.2. Illustration of the difference between somatic and germ-line mutation. Somatic mutations are not passed to the next generation, whereas those in the germ line may be passed to offspring.

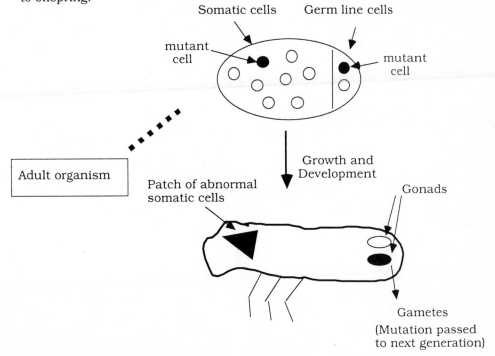

Solutions to Problems and Discussion Questions

1. The term *chromosomal mutation* refers to changes in chromosome number or structure, such as duplications, deletions, inversions, and translocations. A *gene mutation* is a change in the nucleotide sequence of a single gene. Somatic mutations are non-heritable, but potentially hazardous. Gametic mutations are heritable and occur in the germ line.

2. A functional sequence of nucleotides, a gene, is likely to be the product of perhaps a billion or so years of evolution. Each gene and its product function in an environment which has also evolved, or co-evolved.

A coordinated output of each gene product is required for life. Deviations from the norm, caused by mutation, are likely to be disruptive because of the complex and interactive environment in which each gene product must function. However, on occasion a beneficial variation occurs.

3. A diploid organism possesses at least two copies of each gene (except for "hemizygous" genes) and in most cases, the amount of product from one gene of each pair is sufficient for production of a normal phenotype. Recall that the condition of "recessive" is defined by the phenotype of the heterozygote. If one unit of output from the normal gene gives the same phenotype as in the normal homozygote, where there are two units of output, the allele is considered "recessive."

Phenotype, if mutant is:

Genotypes	recessive	dominant
wild/wild	wild	wild
wild/mutant	wild	mutant
mutant/mutant	mutant	mutant

4. Let *II* indicate a *mutagenized* second chromosome

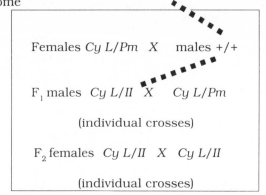

Females *Cy L/Pm*   X   males +/+

F₁ males *Cy L/II* X *Cy L/Pm*

(individual crosses)

F₂ females *Cy L/II* X *Cy L/II*

(individual crosses)

F₃ genotypes:

Cy L/Cy L   (lethal)

Cy L/II   (Curly, Lobe)

II/II   (dies if recessive lethal)

The *II/II* class will be present in crosses where no recessive lethal was introduced. If a recessive lethal had been introduced, only Curly-Lobe (*CyL/II*) flies would be seen in the cultures. In addition, recessive morphological mutations will be expressed in the *II/II* offspring.

5. Watson and Crick recognized that various tautomeric forms, caused by single proton shifts, could exist for the nitrogenous bases of DNA. Such shifts could result in mutations by allowing hydrogen bonding of normally noncomplementary bases during DNA replication. As stated in the text, important tautomers involve keto-enol pairs for thymine and guanine, and amino-imino pairs for cytosine and adenine.

6. Frameshift mutations are likely to change more than one amino acid in a protein product because as the reading frame is shifted, new codons are generated. In addition, there is the possibility that a nonsense triplet could be introduced, thus causing premature chain termination. If a single pyrimidine or purine has been substituted, then only one amino acid is influenced.

7. *Photoreactivation* can lead to repair of UV-induced damage. An enzyme, photoreactivation enzyme, will absorb a photon of light to cleave thymine dimers. *Excision repair* involves the products of several genes, DNA polymerase I, and DNA ligase to clip out the UV-induced dimer, fill in, and join the phosphodiester backbone in the resulting gap. The excision repair process can be activated by damage which distorts the DNA helix.

Recombinational repair is a system which responds to DNA that has escaped other repair mechanisms at the time of replication. If a gap is created on one of the newly synthesized strands, a "rescue operation or SOS response" allows the gap to be filled. Many different gene products are involved in this repair process. In SOS repair, the normal proofreading of DNA polymerase III is suppressed and this therefore is called an "error-prone system."

8. Because mammography involves the use of X-rays and X-rays are known to be mutagenic, it has been suggested that frequent mammograms may do harm. Nevertheless, the risk of cancer from mammograms is more than offset by the benefit of cancer detection.

9. In *excision repair* a small section of DNA is removed, and subsequently "filled-in" by DNA polymerase activity. Such represents "unscheduled DNA synthesis." One can determine complementation groupings by placing each heterokaryon giving a "0" into one group and those giving a "+" into a separate group.

For instance, *XP1* and *XP2* are placed into the same group because they do not complement each other. However, *XP1* and *XP5* do complement ("+"), therefore they are in a different group. Completing such pairings allows one to determine the following groupings:

XP1	*XP4*	*XP5*
XP2		*XP6*
XP3		*XP7*

The groupings (complementation groups) indicate that there are at least three "genes" which form products necessary for unscheduled DNA synthesis. All of the cell lines which are in the same complementation group are defective in the same product.

10. X-rays are of higher energy and shorter wavelength than UV light. They have greater penetrating ability and can create more disruption of DNA.

11. The sequence of bases in a wild type gene provides a code which is eventually translated into the amino acid sequence of a protein. If an insertion sequence or transposable element is inserted into that wild type sequence, the original coding is disrupted, thus leading to a modified (mutant) gene product. In addition, insertion sequences and transposable elements may carry DNA sequences which influence a variety of transcriptional and translational activities.

12. Your study should include examination of the following short-term aspects: immediate assessment of radiation amounts distributed in a grid within the bomb site as well as a control area not receiving bomb-induced radiation, radiation exposure as measured by radiation sickness and evidence of radiation poisoning from tissue samples, abortion rates, birthing rates, and chromosomal studies.

Long-term assessment should include: sex-ratio distortion (males being more influenced by X-linked recessive lethals than females), chromosomal studies, birth and abortion rates, cancer frequency and type, and genetic disorders. In each case data should be compared to the control site to see if changes are bomb-related.

In addition, to attempt to determine cause-effect, it is often helpful to show a dose response. Thus, by comparing the location of individuals at the time of exposure to the matrix of radiation amounts, one may be able to determine whether those most exposed to radiation suffer the most physiologically and genetically. If a positive correlation is observed, then statistically significant conclusions may be possible.

13. Each individual arises from the union of two gametes. If there are 30,000 genes per genome (haploid) then the number of new mutations per individual would be as follows:

$$2(1 \times 10^{-5})(3 \times 10^4) = 0.6$$

Assuming 4.3×10^9 individuals, there would be 2.58×10^9 new mutations in the current populace.

14. Each involves a ballooning of tribnucleotide repeats. See the *Essentials* text for a detailed description of the role of trinucleotide repeats in a variety of human diseases. Genetic anticipation is the occurrence of an earlier age of onset of a genetic disease in successive generations.

15. The cystic fibrosis gene produces a complex membrane transport protein which contains several major domains: a highly conserved ATP binding domain, two hydrophobic domains, and a large cytoplasmic domain which probably serves in a regulatory capacity. The protein is like many ATP-dependent transport systems, some of which have been well studied. When a mutation causes clinical symptoms, fluid secretion is decreased and dehydrated mucus accumulates in the lungs and air passages. Mutations which radically alter the structure of the protein (frameshift, splicing, nonsense, deletions, duplications, *etc.*) would probably have more influence on protein function than those which cause relatively minor amino acid substitutions, although this generalization does not always hold true. A protein with multiple functional domains would be expected to react to mutational insult in a variety of ways.

Chapter 15: Regulation of Gene Expression

Concept Areas	Corresponding Problems
Positive/Negative Control	2, 6
Cis/Trans Acting	4, 5, 6
Induction/Repression	3, 6
Operon Model	1, 4, 5, 6, 16
Catabolite Repression	7, 8
Eukaryotic Regulation	9, 10, 11, 12, 13, 14, 15

Vocabulary and Critical Issues

Structures and Substances

Lactose operon

  structural genes

    lac Z

      β-galactosidase

    lac Y

      β-galactoside permease

    lac A

      transacetylase

  polycistronic mRNA

  gratuitous inducer

  isopropylthiogalactoside (IPTG)

  constitutive mutants

    lac I⁻

    lac Oᶜ

merozygote

repression loop

repressor molecule

  diffusible, cellular (F15.2)

allosteric

  operator region

    no diffusible product

    adjacent control (F15.2)

  lac I^q

  lac I^s

CAP

CAP binding site

  cyclic adenosine monophosphate (cAMP)

  adenyl cyclase

Tryptophan

  tryptophan synthetase

trp R⁻, trp R⁺

structural genes

    trp E, D, C, B, A

    polycistronic mRNA

trp P-trp O region

leader sequence

    attenuator

Promoters

RNA polymerase I, II, III

    TATA box

        TATA-binding protein (TBP)

    CAAT box

    GC box

    enhancers

    transcription factors, TFII...

        TBP-associated factors (TAF)

    upstream activator sequences (UAS)

    DNA binding domains
      (structural motifs)

        trans-activating domain

        helix-turn-helix (HTH)

        leucine zipper (bZIP)

        homeobox

        zinc fingers

           homeodomains

    nucleosome

        SWI, SNF

homeotic genes

    DNA methylation

    Barr body

steroid hormones

    receptor protein

    ecdysone

    hormone responsive element (HRE)

Processing transcripts

    alternative processing

        preprotachykinin mRNA
          (PPT mRNA)

          tachykinin P, K

        α-tropomyosin

Processes/Methods

Genetic regulation

    inducible

        lactose

    repressible

        tryptophan

          attenuation

    negative control (F15.1)

        catabolite repression

    positive control (F15.1)

        constitutive

    allosteric

    equilibrium dialysis

Transcriptional control

    Immunoglobin genetics

    Chromatin remodeling acetylation

    Posttranscriptional regulation

    Posttranslational regulation

Concepts

Genetic regulation

    cis/trans acting

    efficiency

        activity of enzymes

        level of transcription

Positive control (F15.1)

Negative control (F15.1)

    lactose operon

    induction

    catabolite repression

    tryptophan

      co-repressor

      repression

      attenuation

Operon model

Eukaryotic regulation

    chromatin conformation

    transcriptional

      homeotic genes

    posttranscriptional

    processing

    transport

    translation

    DNA methylation

Hormone relationships

Chapter 15

F15.1. Illustration of general processes of *negative* and *positive* control. In *negative* control, the regulatory protein inhibits transcription while under *positive* control, transcription is stimulated.

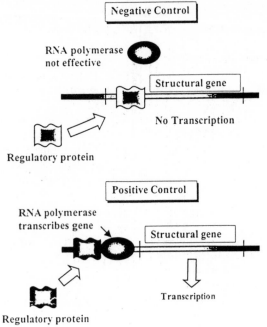

F15.2. Illustration of the nature of the product of the *I* gene. It can act "at a distance" because it is a protein which can diffuse through the cytoplasm and thus act in "trans" as well as in "cis." There is no protein product of the operator gene, therefore it can only act in "cis."

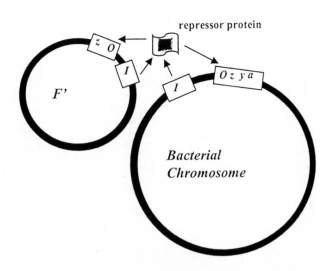

Solutions to Problems and Discussion Questions

1. The answer to this question is a key to enhancing a student's understanding of the Jacob-Monod model as related to lactose and tryptophan metabolism. The enzymes of the lactose operon are needed to break down and use lactose as an energy source. If lactose is the sole carbon source, the enzymes are synthesized *to use* that carbon source. With no lactose present, there is no "need" for the enzymes.

The tryptophan operon contains structural genes for the *synthesis* of tryptophan. If there is little or no tryptophan in the medium, the tryptophan operon is "turned on" to manufacture tryptophan. If tryptophan is abundant in the medium, then there is no "need" for the operon to be manufacturing "tryptophan synthetases."

2. Refer to F15.1 to see that under *negative* control, the regulatory molecule interferes with transcription, while in *positive* control, the regulatory molecule stimulates transcription. Negative control is seen in the *lactose* and *tryptophan* systems.

3. In an *inducible system*, the repressor which normally interacts with the operator to inhibit transcription is inactivated by an *inducer*, thus permitting transcription. In a *repressible system*, a normally inactive repressor is *activated* by a *co-repressor*, thus enabling it (the activated repressor) to bind to the operator to inhibit transcription. Because the interaction of the protein (repressor) has a negative influence on transcription, the systems described here are forms of *negative control* (see F15.1).

4. Refer to the *Essentials* text and to F15.2 to get a good understanding of the lactose system before starting.

$I^+ O^+ Z^+$ = **Inducible** because a repressor protein can interact with the operator to turn off transcription.

$I^- O^+ Z^+$ = **Constitutive** because the repressor gene is mutant, therefore no repressor protein is available.

$I^+ O^c Z^+$ = **Constitutive** because even though a repressor protein is made, it cannot bind with the mutant operator.

$I^- O^+ Z^+ / F' I^+$ = **Inducible** because even though there is one mutant repressor gene, the other I^+ gene, on the F factor, produces a normal repressor protein which is diffusible and capable of interacting with the operon to repress transcription.

$I^+ O^c Z^+ / F' O^+$ = **Constitutive** because there is a constitutive operator (O^c) next to a normal Z gene. Remembering that this operator functions in *cis* and is not influenced by the repressor protein, constitutive synthesis of β-galactosidase will occur.

$I^s O^+ Z^+$ = **Repressed** because the product of the I^s gene is *insensitive* to the inducer lactose and thus cannot be inactivated. The repressor will continually interact with the operator and shut off transcription regardless of the presence or absence of lactose.

$I^s O^+ Z^+ / F' I^+$ = **Repressed** because, as in the previous case, the product of the I^s gene is *insensitive* to the inducer lactose and thus cannot be inactivated. The repressor will continually interact with the operator and shut off transcription regardless of the presence or absence of lactose. The fact that there is a normal I^+ gene is of no consequence because once a repressor from I^s binds to an operator, the presence of normal repressor molecules will make no difference.

5. Refer to the *Essentials* text and to F 13.2 to get a good understanding of the lactose system before starting.

$I^+ O^+ Z^+$ = Because of the function of the active repressor from the I^+ gene, and no lactose to influence its function, there will be **No Enzyme Made.**

$I^+ O^c Z^+$ = There will be a **Functional Enzyme Made** because the constitutive operator is in *cis* with a Z gene. The lactose in the medium will have no influence because of the constitutive operator. The repressor cannot bind to the mutant operator.

$I^- O^+ Z^-$ = There will be a **Nonfunctional Enzyme Made** because with i the system is constitutive but the z gene is mutant. The absence of lactose in the medium will have no influence because of the non-functional repressor. The mutant repressor cannot bind to the operator.

$I^- O^+ Z^-$ = There will be a **Nonfunctional Enzyme Made** because with i the system is constitutive but the z gene is mutant. The lactose in the medium will have no influence because of the non-functional repressor. The mutant repressor cannot bind to the operator.

$I^- O^+ Z^+ / F' \ I^+$ = There will be **No Enzyme Made** because in the absence of lactose, the repressor product of the I^+ gene will bind to the operator and inhibit transcription.

$I^+ O^c Z^+ / F' \ O^+$ = Because there is a constitutive operator in *cis* with a normal z gene, there will be **Functional Enzyme Made.** The lactose in the medium will have no influence because of the mutant operator.

$I^+ O^+ Z^- / F' \ I^+ O^+ Z^+$ = Because there is lactose in the medium, the repressor protein will not bind to the operator and transcription will occur. The presence of a normal z gene allows a **Functional and Non-functional Enzyme to be Made.** The repressor protein is diffusable, working in *trans*.

$I^- O^+ Z^- / F' \ I^+ O^+ Z^+$ = Because there is no lactose in the medium, the repressor protein (from I^+) will repress the operators and there will be **No Enzyme Made.**

$I^s \ O^+ \ Z^+ / F' \ O^+$ = With the product of I^s there is binding of the repressor to the operator and therefore **No Enzyme Made.** The lack of lactose in the medium is of no consequence because the mutant repressor is insensitive to lactose.

$I^+ O^c Z^+ / F' \ O^+ \ Z^+$ = The arrangement of the constitutive operator (O^c) with the normal Z gene will cause a **Functional Enzyme to be Made.** In addition, the normal repressor will be inactivated by the lactose and the unit residing in the F factor will produce a **Functional Enzyme.**

6. First notice that in the first row of data, the presence of tm in the medium causes the production of active enzyme from the wild type arrangement of genes. From this one would conclude that the system is *inducible*. To determine which gene is the structural gene, look for the IE function and see that it is related to c^-. Therefore, c codes for the **structural gene.** Because when b is mutant, no enzyme is produced, b must be the **promoter.**

Notice that when genes a and d are mutant, constitutive synthesis occurs, therefore one must be the operator and the other gene codes for the repressor protein. To distinguish these functions, one must remember that the repressor operates as a diffusible substance and can be on the host chromosome or the F factor (functioning in *trans*). However, the operator can only operate in *cis*. In addition, in *cis*, the constitutive operator is dominant to its wild type allele, while the mutant repressor is recessive to its wild type allele.

Notice that the mutant a gene is dominant to its wild type allele, whereas the mutant d allele is recessive (behaving as wild type in the first row). Therefore, the a locus is the **operator** and the d locus is the **repressor** gene.

7. In order to understand this question, it is necessary that you understand the negative regulation of the lactose operon by the *lac* repressor as well as the positive control exerted by the CAP protein. Remember, if lactose is present, it inactivates the *lac* repressor. If glucose is present, it inhibits adenyl cyclase thereby reducing, through a lowering of cAMP levels, the positive action of CAP on the *lac* operon.

(a) With no lactose and no glucose, the operon is off because the *lac* repressor is bound to the operator and although CAP is bound to its binding site, it will not override the action of the repressor.

(b) With lactose added to the medium, the *lac* repressor is inactivated and the operon is transcribing the structural genes. With no glucose, the CAP is bound to its binding site, thus enhancing transcription.

(c) With no lactose present in the medium, the *lac* repressor is bound to the operator region, and since glucose inhibits adenyl cyclase, the CAP protein will not interact with its binding site. The operon is therefore "off."

(d) With lactose present, the *lac* repressor is inactivated, however since glucose is also present, CAP will not interact with its binding site. Under this condition transcription is severely diminished and the operon can be considered to be "off."

8. (a) Because activated CAP is a component of the cooperative binding of RNA polymerase to the *lac* promoter, absence of a functional *crp* would compromise the positive control exhibited by CAP

(b) Without a CAP binding site there would be a reduction in the inducibility of the *lac* operon.

9. There are several reasons for anticipating a variety of different regulatory mechanisms in eukaryotes as compared to prokaryotes. Eukaryotic cells contain greater amounts of DNA and this DNA is associated with various proteins, including histones and nonhistone chromosomal proteins.

Chromatin as such does not exist in prokaryotes. In addition, whereas there is usually only one chromosome in prokaryotes, eukaryotes have more than one chromosome all enclosed in a membrane (nuclear membrane). This nuclear membrane separates, both temporally and spatially, the processes of transcription and translation, thus providing an opportunity for post-transcriptional, pre-translational regulation.

While prokaryotes respond genetically to changes in their external environment, cells of multicellular eukaryotes interact with each other as well as the external environment. The structural and functional diversity of cells of a multicellular eukaryote, coupled with the finding that all cells of an organism contain a complete complement of genes, suggests that in some cells certain genes are active which are not active in other cells.

It is often difficult to study eukaryotic gene regulation because of the complexities mentioned above, especially tissue specificity and the various levels at which regulation can occur. Obtaining a homogeneous group of cells from a multicellular organism often requires a significant alteration of the natural environment of the cell. Thus, results from studies on isolated cells must be interpreted with caution. In addition, because of the variety of intracellular components (nuclear and cytoplasmic) it is difficult to isolate, free of contamination, certain molecular species. Even if such isolation is accomplished, it is difficult to interpret the actual behavior of such molecules in an artificial environment.

10. *Organization of DNA*: Changes in DNA/chromosome structure can influence overall gene output.

Transcription: There are several factors which are known to influence transcription: *promoters*, TATA, CAAT, and GC boxes, as well as other upstream regulatory sequences; *enhancers*, which are *cis*-acting sequences that act at various locations and orientations; *transcription factors*, with various structural motifs (zinc fingers, homeodomains, and leucine zippers) which bind DNA and influence transcription; *receptor-hormone complexes* which influence transcription.

Processing and transport types of regulation involve the efficiency of hnRNA maturation as related to capping, polyA tail addition, and intron removal.

Translation: After mRNAs are produced from the processing of hnRNA, they have the potential of being translated. The stability of the mRNAs appears to be an additional regulatory control point. Certain factors, such as protein subunits, may influence a variety of steps in the translational mechanism. For instance, a protein or protein subunit may activate an RNAse, which will degrade certain mRNAs or a particular regulatory element may cause a ribosome to stall, thus decreasing the speed of translation and increasing the exposure of a mRNA to the action of RNAses.

11. *Promoters* are conserved DNA sequences which influence transcription from the "upstream" side (5') of mRNA coding genes. They are usually fixed in position and within 100 base pairs of the initiation site for mRNA synthesis. Examples of such promoters are the following: TATA, CAAT, and GC boxes.

Enhancers are *cis*-acting sequences of DNA which stimulate the transcription from most, if not all, promoters. They are somewhat different from promoters in that the position of the enhancer need not be fixed; it may be upstream, downstream, or within the gene being regulated. The orientation may be inverted without significantly influencing its action. Enhancers can work ondifferent genes, that is, they are not gene-specific.

12. Transcription factors are modular structures which are not part of the RNA polymerase but are needed for the initiation of transcription. They generally have two functional domains: one that binds to DNA and the other that activates transcription through a variety of protein-protein interactions.

13. Steroid hormones enter a target cell and bind to a specific receptor protein in the cytoplasm. The hormone-receptor complex moves to the nucleus and activates transcription of one or more specific genes.

14. Alteration of chromatin structure through interaction of enhancers with a variety of transcription factors creates bending or looping which has regulatory capacity. In altered configurations transcription can be stimulated. By contrast, posttranscriptional forms of regulation include modification of the RNA product: 5' capping, 3' polyadenylation, intron removal, and alternative processing. In addition, a variety of proceses influence mRNA's availability for translation; stability, altrenative processing, *etc.*

15. Your response should deal with the following issues:

- differences in basic chromosome structure
- differences in gene structure
- cell structure (nucleus in eukaryotes)
- levels of potential regulation
 . . .transcriptional
 . . .mRNA processing
 . . .transport
 . . .selection for processing and translation
 . . .mRNA stability
 . . .posttranslational processing
- genomic aspects (amplification, *etc.*)
- biological context in terms of multicellular
 interactions *versus* single cell survival
- operons and mRNA synthesis

16. The first two sentences in the problem indicate an inducible system where oil stimulates the production of a protein(?) which turns on (positive control) genes to metabolize oil. The different results in strains #2 and #4 suggest a *cis*-acting system. Because the operon by itself (when mutant as in strain #3) gives constitutive synthesis of the structural genes, *cis*-acting system is also supported. The *cis*-acting element is most likely part of the operon.

Chapter 16: Recombinant DNA Technology

Concept Areas	Corresponding Problems
Gene Cloning	1, 2, 3, 4, 10
Vectors	5
Restriction Mapping	6, 7, 9
Probing	8
DNA Sequencing	12
DNA Fingerprinting	11

Vocabulary and Critical Issues

Structures and Substances

Recombinant DNA

    Restriction endonucleases (enzyme)

      Eco R1

    E. coli K12

    Saccharomyces cerevisiae

Vector

    clone

    cloning vehicle

      plasmids

        pUC18

        polylinker

        lacZ

        X-gal

    bacteriophage (lambda)

    YAC (yeast artificial chromosome)

ARS (autonomously replicating sequence)

cDNA (complementary DNA)

Reverse transcriptase

DNA polymerase I

S_1 nuclease

open reading frame (ORF)

oligonucleotide

primer

heat-stable DNA polymerase

RFLP
(restriction fragment length polymorphism)

dideoxynucleotide

Processes/Methods

Recombinant DNA technology

    gene splicing

    genetic engineering

recombinant DNA

    restriction endonucleases

PCR analysis

  denaturation

  annealing of specific primers

  oligonucleotides

  extension of primers

Library construction

  genomic libraries

    chromosome-specific libraries

    cDNA libraries

      reverse transcriptase

      DNA polymerase I

      S_1 nuclease

      rapid amplification of cDNA ends (RACE)

  replica plating

    recovery of recombinant clones

      probes

colony and plaque hybridization

chromosome walking

chromosome jumping

open reading frames (ORF)

restriction mapping

  gel electrophoresis

nucleic acid blotting

  Southern blot

    autoradiography

    Northern blot, Western blot

  DNA sequencing

Concepts

Gene cloning

Probing

Restriction mapping

Sequencing

Gene mapping

DNA fingerprinting

  RFLP analysis

Chapter 16

Solutions to Problems and Discussion Questions

1. Recombinant DNA technology, also called genetic engineering or gene splicing, involves the creation of associations of DNA that are not typically found in nature. Particular enzymes, called *restriction endonucleases*, cut DNA at specific sites and often yield "sticky" ends for additional interaction with DNA molecules cut with the same class of enzyme. A *vector* may be a plasmid, bacteriophage, or cosmid which receives, through ligation, a piece, or pieces of foreign DNA. The recombinant vector can transform (or transfect) a host cell (bacterium, yeast cell, etc.) and be amplified in number.

2. *Reverse transcriptase* is often used to promote the formation of cDNA (complementary DNA) from a mRNA molecule. Eukaryotic mRNAs typically have a 3' polyA tail as indicated in the diagram below. The poly dT segment provides a double-stranded section which serves to prime the production of the complementary strand.

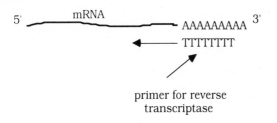

primer for reverse
transcriptase

3. When the *insulin* gene is "manufactured," it is made as a complementary copy of the mRNA, which is void of introns. Therefore, the insulin mRNA which is made from the cDNA does not have introns.

4. The question of protein/DNA recognition and interaction is a difficult one to answer. Much research has been done to attempt to understand the nature of the specificity of such interactions. In general it is believed that the protein interacts with the major groove of the DNA helix. This information comes from the structure of the few proteins which have been sufficiently well studied to suggest that the DNA major groove and "fingers" or extensions of the protein form the basis of interaction.

5. Even though there is great economic potential in achieving sophisticated genetic engineering in plants, there are relatively few cloning vectors available for economically important crops.

6. The segment contains the palindromic sequence below which is recognized by the restriction enzyme *Bam*HI.

CCTAGG
GGATCC

7. Assuming a random distribution of all four bases, the four-base sequence would occur on average every 256 base pairs (4^4), the six-base sequence every 4096 base pairs, and the eight-base sequence every 65,536 base pairs. One might use an eight-base restriction enzyme to produce relatively few large fragments. If one wanted to construct an eukaryotic genome library, such large fragments would have to be cloned into special vectors, such as yeast artificial chromosomes.

8. A typical procedure is outlined in the *Essentials* text. A filter is used to bind the DNA from the colonies and a labeled probe is used to detect, through hybridization, the DNA of interest. Cells with the desired clone are then picked from the original plate and the plasmid is isolated from the cells.

9. The problem can be best solved by drawing out the strands, then placing the restriction sites in the appropriate positions as follows:

enzyme I   350 | 950

enzyme II 200| 1100

To determine the orientation of the restriction sites to each other, examine the results of the double digested DNA and note that there is a 150bp fragment meaning that enzyme II cuts within the 350pb fragment of enzyme I. Therefore, the final map is as follows:

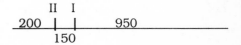

message is often lost.

10. There may be several factors contributing to the lack of representation of the 5' end of the mRNA. One has to do with the possibility that the reverse transcriptase may not completely synthesize the DNA from the RNA template. The other reason may be that the 3' end of the copied DNA tends to fold back on itself, thus providing a primer for the DNA polymerase. Additional preparation of the cDNA requires some digestion at the folded region. Since this folded region corresponds to the 5' end of the mRNA, some of the

11. Option (b) is fully compatible with the data provided because both bands in the offspring are found in both parents.

12. With repeated sequences in the genome, chromosome walking is complicated because the clone hybridizes to multiple regions. One can "chromosome jump" over repeated sequences. One can block repeats by addition of complementary repetitive DNA.

Chapter 17: Chromosome Structure and DNA Sequence Organization

Concept Areas

Corresponding Problems

Viral and Bacterial Chromosomes   1, 11, 12

Mitochondrial and Chloroplast DNA   2, 8

Organization of DNA in Chromatin   6, 7, 9, 10, 13

Organization of the Eukaryotic Genome   3, 4, 5

Vocabulary and Critical Issues

Structures and Substances

Viral chromosomes

    DNA, RNA

       double-stranded, single-stranded

       circular, linear

    protein coat

    ϕX174, polyoma, lambda (λ)

Bacterial chromosomes

    DNA

    double-stranded

    nucleoid

    E. coli

       circular

DNA-binding proteins

    HU, H

Mitochondrial DNA (mtDNA)

    plant, animal

    coding (mtDNA)

       rRNAs, tRNAs

       respiratory components

    coding (nuclear)

       imported products

Chloroplast DNA (cpDNA)

    circular, double-stranded

    different than nuclear DNA

    coding (cpDNA)

       rRNAs, tRNAs

       ribulose-1-5-bisphosphate carboxylase

Eukaryotic chromosomes

    chromatin

    mitotic chromosomes

       condensed chromatin

          folded fiber

specialized chromosomes

    polytene

      chromomeres

      1000-5000 DNA strands

      puff

      autoradiography

    lampbrush, lateral loops

nucleoprotein

histones

    amino acid composition

    tetramers

      nucleosome core particle

nonhistones

    solenoid

Heterochromatin, euchromatin

    telomeric DNA sequences

    telomere-associated sequences

    satellite and repetitive DNA

pseudogene

centromeric DNA (CEN) I, II, III

    alphoid family

VNTR (variable number tandem repeat)

    minisatellite, microsatellite

moderately (middle) repetitive DNA

short interspersed elements (SINES)

    Alu family

long interspersed elements (LINES), L1

repetitive transposed sequences

    moderately repetitive multicopy genes

    rRNA related

Processes/Methods

Supercoiling

    packing ratio

Uniparental mode of inheritance

Importing of nuclear-coded gene products

Autoradiography

Folded-fiber (eukaryotic chromosome)

    coiling-twisting-condensing

Euchromatin

Heterochromatin

    few genes, late replicating

    position effect

In situ hybridization

DNA fingerprinting

Transposition

Concepts

Variety of chromosomal conformations

Evolution of cellular organelles

    endosymbiont hypothesis

Heterochromatin/euchromatin

Centromeric structure

Repetitive DNA

Solutions to Problems and Discussion Questions

1. General similarities and differences:

Viral	Bacterial
DNA or RNA	DNA
single-stranded	double-stranded
double-stranded	circular (*E. coli*)
linear	DNA-binding proteins
ring shaped (circular)	genome size >100µm
naked nucleic acid	
genome size < 100µm	

2. General similarities and differences:

mtDNA	cpDNA
circular	circular
double-stranded	double-stranded
semiconservative repl.	semiconservative repl.
animal (16 to 18 kb)	>100 kb
plant (>100 kb)	genes(rRNAs, tRNAs, etc.)
genes (rRNAs, tRNAs, etc.)	
diverse (introns in some)	
variations in genetic code	

3. Polytene chromosomes are formed from numerous DNA replications, pairing of homologues, and absence of strand separation or cytoplasmic division.

4. Puffs represent active genes as evidenced by staining and uptake of labeled RNA precursors as assayed by autoradiography.

5. Lampbrush chromosomes are typically present in vertebrate oocytes (meiotic genetic processes).

6. While greater DNA content per cell is associated with eukaryotes, one can not universally equate genomic size with an increase in organismic complexity. There are numerous examples where DNA content per cell varies considerably among closely related species. Because of the diverse cell types of multicellular eukaryotes, a variety of gene products is required, which may be related to the increase in DNA content per cell. In addition, the advantage of diploidy automatically increases DNA content per cell. However, seeing the question in another way, it is likely that a much higher *percentage* of the genome of a prokaryote is actually involved in phenotype production than in a eukaryote.

Eukaryotes have evolved the capacity to obtain and maintain what appears to be large amounts of "extra" perhaps "junk" DNA. This concept will be examined in subsequent chapters of the text. Prokaryotes on the other hand, with their relatively short life cycle, are extremely efficient in their accumulation and use of their genome.

Given the larger amount of DNA per cell and the requirement that the DNA be partitioned in an orderly fashion to daughter cells during cell division, certain mechanisms and structures (mitosis, nucleosomes, centromeres, etc.) have evolved for *packaging* the DNA. In addition, the genome is divided into separate entities (chromosomes) to perhaps facilitate the partitioning process in mitosis and meiosis.

7. Digestion of chromatin with endonucleases, such as micrococcal nuclease, gives DNA fragments of approximately 200 base pairs or multiples of such. X-ray diffraction data indicated a regular spacing of DNA in chromatin. Regularly spaced bead-like structures (nucleosomes) were identified by electron microscopy. Nucleosomes are octomeric structures of two molecules of each histone (H2A, H2B, H3, and H4) except H1. Between the nucleosomes and complexed with linker DNA is histone H1. A 146-base pair sequence of DNA wraps around the nucleosome and as chromosome condensation occurs a 300-Å fiber is formed. It appears to be composed of 5 or 6 nucleosomes coiled together. Such a structure is called a solenoid.

8. The endosymbiont theory states that mitochondria and chloroplasts evolved from free-living bacteria-like structures that entered a symbiotic relationship with a host cell. In time, both the bacteria-like particle and the host cell became interdependent through the loss and sharing of products. In addition to the size (sedimentation properties) of ribosomes, the ribosomes of mitochondria and chloroplasts show antibiotic sensitivity which is similar to present-day bacteria, thus supporting the endosymbiont theory.

9. *Heterochromatin* is chromosomal material which stains deeply and remains condensed when other parts of chromosomes, euchromatin, are otherwise pale and decondensed. Heterochromatic regions replicate late in S phase and are relatively inactive in a genetic sense because there are few genes present or if they are present, they are repressed. Telomeres and the areas adjacent to centromeres are composed of heterochromatin.

10. (a) Since there are 200 base pairs per nucleosome (as defined in this problem) and 10^9 base pairs, there would be 5×10^6 nucleosomes.

(b) Given that there are 6 nucleosomes per solenoid, there would be 0.833×10^6 solenoids.

(c) Since there are 5×10^6 nucleosomes and nine histones (including H1) per nucleosome, there must be $9(5 \times 10^6)$ histone molecules: 4.5×10^7.

(d) Since there are 10^9 base pairs present and each base pair is 3.4 Å the overall length of the DNA is 3.4×10^9 Å. Dividing this value by the packing ratio (50) gives 6.8×10^7 Å.

11. The first part of this problem is to convert all of the given values to cubic Å remembering that 1 μm = 10,000 Å. Using the formula πr^2 for the area of a circle and $4/3 \pi r^3$ for the volume of a sphere, the following calculations apply:

Volume of DNA: 3.14×10Å $\times 10$Å $\times (50 \times 10^4$Å$)$ $= 1.57 \times 10^8$Å^3

Volume of capsid: $4/3 (3.14 \times 400$Å $\times 400$Å $\times 400$Å$) = 2.67 \times 10^8$Å^3

Because the capsid head has a greater volume than the volume of DNA, the DNA will fit into the capsid.

12. One base pair occupies 0.34nm, therefore the equation would be as follows:

$$52\mu m/(0.34nm/bp) \times 1000nm/\mu m =$$

$$152,941 \text{ base pairs}$$

13. Volume of the nucleus = $4/3 \pi r^3$

$$= 4/3 \times 3.14 \times (5 \times 10^3 nm)^3$$

$$= 5.23 \times 10^{11} nm^3$$

Volume of the chromosome = $\pi r^2 \times$ length

$$= 3.14 \times 5.5nm \times 5.5nm \times (2 \times 10^9 nm)$$

$$= 1.9 \times 10^{11} nm^3$$

Therefore, the percentage of the volume of the nucleus occupied by the chromatin is

$$= 1.9 \times 10^{11} nm^3 / 5.23 \times 10^{11} nm^3 \times 100$$

$$= \text{about } 36.3\%$$

Chapter 18: Genomics and Proteomics

Concept Areas	Corresponding Problems
Genomic Organization	1, 2, 3
Multigene Families	4, 5, 6, 7

Vocabulary and Critical Issues

Structures and Substances

Genome

  Pseudomonas aeruginosa

Bacterial chromosomes

  DNA

  double-stranded

  circular, linear

  plasmids

  polycistronic

  high density

    approximately 1 gene/kb

  operons

Viruses

  overlapping genes

Archaea (archaebacteria)

  rDNA sequence comparisons

  extremophiles

    circular, double stranded DNA

  histones

  introns (tRNA genes)

Eukaryote

  variable gene density

  introns

  repetitive sequences

  Caenorhabditis elegans

    6 chromosomes

    20,000 genes

    repetitive DNA

    introns

  higher plants

    Arabidopsis thaliana

  humans

    3 billion nucleotides

    protein-coding about 5%

    transposable elements (LINE, Alu)

    gene desert

    30,000-40,000 genes

  multigene families

    alpha-globin (2)

      zeta

pseudogene

  beta-globin

    paralogous

  intergenic regions

  epsilon

  gamma (Gγ, Aγ)

  delta

  beta

Immunoglobin genes

  antigen

  antibody

  B-cell

    lymphocyte

  epitope

  IgM, IgD, IgG, IgA, IgE

  heavy chain (H)

  variable region

  constant region (C)

  light chain (L)

    kappa

    lambda

  antibody combining site

  leader variable region (L-V)

  joining region (J)

  constant region (C)

Histone genes

  tandem repeats

  lack introns

  polarity of transcription

  sequence conservation

Inteins

Bacterial proteome

Nuclear pore complex

Processes/Methods

Genomics

Proteomics

Human Genome Project (HGP)

Human Genome Organization (HUGO)

  clone-by-clone

  shotgun method

ELSI (ethical, legal, and social aspects)

TIGR (The Institute for Genome Research)

  annotation

  open reading frame (ORF)

  ATG

  TAA, TAG, TGA

  3'AATAAA poly A signal

  CpG

Genome contraction

Genome evolution

Chapter 18

Genome duplication

Gene duplication

    unequal crossing over

    sister chromatid exchange

    unequal sister chromatid exchange

    replication errors

Imprecise joining

Break-nibble-add

Sequence conservation

Proteomics

    peptide mass fingerprinting

Concepts

Genomics

Proteomics

Genome organization comparisons

Genome evolution

Minimum genome size (250-350)

Relationships:

    Archaea

    Eubacteria

    Eukaryotes

  Multigene families

    globin genes

    immunoglobin genes

    histone genes

Sequence conservation

Chapter 18

Solutions to Problems and Discussion Questions

1. General similarities and differences:

Yeast	Bacterial
DNA	DNA
double-stranded	double-stranded
chromosomes	circular (*E. coli*)
12 MB	naked nucleic acid
6548 genes	4.6 MB
	4397 genes

2. While greater DNA content per cell is associated with eukaryotes, one can not universally equate genomic size with an increase in organismic complexity. There are numerous examples where DNA content per cell varies considerably among closely related species. Because of the diverse cell types of multicellular eukaryotes, a variety of gene products is required, which may be related to the increase in DNA content per cell. In addition, the advantage of diploidy automatically increases DNA content per cell. However, seeing the question in another way, it is likely that a much higher *percentage* of the genome of a prokaryote is actually involved in phenotype production than in a eukaryote. Eukaryotes have evolved the capacity to obtain and maintain what appears to be large amounts of "extra" perhaps "junk" DNA. This concept will be examined in subsequent chapters of the text. Prokaryotes on the other hand, with their relatively short life cycle, are extremely efficient in their accumulation and use of their genome. Given the larger amount of DNA per cell and the requirement that the DNA be partitioned in an orderly fashion to daughter cells during cell division, certain mechanisms and structures (mitosis, nucleosomes, centromeres, etc.) have evolved for *packaging* the DNA. In addition, the genome is divided into separate entities (chromosomes) to perhaps facilitate the partitioning process in mitosis and meiosis.

3. Bacterial genes are densely packed in the chromosome. The protein-coding genes are mostly organized in polycistronic transcription units without introns. Eukaryotic genes are less densely packed in chromosomes and protein-coding genes are mostly organized as single transcription units with introns.

4. While the β-globin gene family is a relatively large (60kb) sequence and restriction analyses show that it is composed of six genes, one is a pseudogene and therefore does not produce a product. The five functional genes each contain two similarly-sized introns which when included with non-coding flanking regions (5' and 3'), and spacer DNA between genes, accounts for the 95% mentioned in the question.

5. V_L = variable region of the light chain, C_H = constant region of the heavy chain, IgG = an immunoglobin class which represents approximately 80% of the antibodies in the blood. J = genes that specify a portion of the V region which includes a portion of the hypervariable region. D = a region between V and J in the heavy immunoglobin chain.

6. The number of combinations is determined by a simple multiplication of the number of genes in each class: V X D X J X C. Thus in this case the answer would be 10 V X 30 D X 50 J X 3 C = 45,000.

7. Again, notice in the *Insights and Solutions* section in this chapter, the total number of combinations is determined by simple multiplication. In this case, for the heavy chain 5 V X 10 D X 20 J = 1000, and for the light chain 10 V X 100 J = 1000. The final total would be 1000 X 1000 = 10^6.

Chapter 19: Biotechnology and Its Implications for Society

Concept Areas	Corresponding Problems
Mapping	4, 5, 6
Diagnosing and Screening Genetic Disorders	7, 8, 10
Gene Therapy	3, 9, 11, 12
Genome Analysis	5
Biotechnology	1, 2, 11

Vocabulary and Critical Issues

Structures and Substances

RFLP

Centimorgan (cM)

Type 1 neurofibromastosis (NF1)

Neurofibromin

β-globin

Allele-specific oligonucleotide (ASO)

Cystic fibrosis

    cystic fibrosis transmembrane
        conductance regulator (CFTR)

DNA (microarray) chips

*BRCA*1

ELSI (Ethical, Legal, and Social Implications
    Program)

Severe combined immunodeficiency (SCID)

    adenosine deaminase

Familial hypercholesterolemia

Cystic fibrosis

Gene therapy vectors

    maloney

    AAV

DNA fingerprint

Minisatellite

    variable number tandem repeat (VNTR)

Insulin

Fusion polypeptide

α-1-antitripsin

    emphysema

Transgenic crops

    glyphosate

    edible vaccines

Dolly

Polly

Processes/Methods

Gene mapping

    RFLP (markers)

    linkage analysis

Lod score method

    (logarithm of the odds)

Positional cloning

    exclusion map

Diagnosis and Screening

    amniocentesis

    chorionic villus sampling

DNA chips and genetic screening (testing)

Gene therapy

    SCID, *etc.*

    ADA

    somatic

    germ-line

    enhancement gene

DNA fingerprinting

    forensic applications

Genome projects

    prokaryotes

    eukaryotes

    Human Genome Project (HGP)

    Human Genome Organization (HGO)

Pharmaceutical applications

    Insulin production

    transgenic organisms

    herbicide-resistance crops

    vaccine production

Concepts

Gene Mapping

Diagnosis

Screning

Genetic testing (ethics)

Gene therapy

DNA fingerprinting

Genome projects (ethics)

Transgenic organisms (ethics)

Solutions to Problems
and Discussion Questions

1. The nature of the digestion process is the breakdown of foodstuffs for eventual absorption by the small intestine. Antigens are usually quite large molecules, and in the process of digestion, they are sometimes broken down into smaller molecules, thus becoming ineffective in stimulating the immune system.

Some individuals are allergic to the food they eat, testifying to the fact that all antigens are not completely degraded or modified by digestion. In some cases, ingested antigens do indeed stimulate the immune system (oral polio vaccine) and provide a route for immunization. Localized (intestinal) immunity can sometimes be stimulated by oral introduction of antigens and in some cases this can offer immunity to ingested pathogens.

2. Glyphosate (a herbicide) inhibits EPSP, a chloroplast enzyme involved in the synthesis of the amino acids phenylalanine, tyrosine, and tryptophan. To generate glyphosate resistance in crop plants, a fusion gene was created which introduced a viral promoter to control the EPSP synthetase gene. The fusion product was placed into the Ti vector and transferred to *A. tumifaciens* which was used to infect crop cells. Calluses were selected on the basis of their resistance to glyphosate. Resistant calluses were later developed into transgenic plants.

There is a remote possibility that such an "accident" can occur. However, in retracing the steps to generate the resistant plant in the first place, it seems more likely that the trait will not "escape" from the plant; rather that the engineered *A. tumifaciens* may escape, infect and transfer glyphosate resistance to pest species.

3. (a,b) One of the main problems with gene therapy is delivery of the desired virus to the target tissue in an effective manner. Several of the problems involving the use of retroviral vectors are the following. (1) Integration into the host must be cell specific so as not to damage non-target cells. (2) Retroviral integration into host cell genomes only occurs if the host cell is replicating.

(3) Insertion of the viral genome might influence non-target but essential genes. (4) Retroviral genomes have a low cloning capacity and cannot carry large inserted sequences as are many human genes. (5) There is a possibility that recombination with host viruses will produce an infectious virus which may do harm.

(c) The question posed here plays on the practical versus the ethical. It would certainly be more efficient (although perhaps more difficult technically) to engineer germ tissue, for once it is done in a family, the disease would be eliminated. However, there are considerable ethical problems associated with germ plasm therapy. It recalls previous attempts of the eugenics movements of past decades which involved the use of selective breeding to purify the human stock. Some present-day biologists have said publically that germ line gene therapy will *not* be conducted.

(d) Overall, there seem to be fewer ethical problems associated with somatic cell gene therapy because there is no permanent alteration in the human gene pool. It is viewed as similar to the practice of modern medicine. However, modification of the germ line stimulates discussion of permanent alteration of the human gene pool and most find this approach undesirable.

4. *Drosophila* is a unique experimental organism in that there is a vast knowledge of its genetics, it is easily cultured and genetically manipulated, and it contains unique chromosomes, polytene chromosomes, which allow visual landmarks. Coupled with probe-labeling (sequence tagged sites), the visible landmarks (chromomeres) and ease of manipulation allow one to actually see where important genes are located in chromosomes. *Drosophila* also contains P elements which allow sequence markers to be inserted into the genome. Microdissection of chromosomes is also useful in developing specific clones for sequencing.

In addition, techniques have been developed (*in situ* hybridization) to allow scientists to actually determine the distributions of gene activities in all tissues of the organism.

5. Positional cloning is a technique whereby the linkage group of a genetic disorder is determined by association of certain RFLP (as markers). A more precise location is obtained by association (linkage studies in kindreds) with additional RFLP markers. Once the general region of the gene is located, sequencing is employed to identify the genes within the general region. Comparison of the sequences in individuals with and without the affliction allows the identification of the gene responsible for the disease. Difficulties in positional cloning relate to the availability of sufficient RFLP markers in the region of the gene and sufficient kindreds to do the actual genetic association of the gene in question to the RFLP markers. Mutations which would speed the process would be those which are most easily seen, perhaps those which change the banding patterns of chromsomes (deletions, duplication, inversions. translocations) or those which cause sufficient base changes which would alter probe hybridization.

6. Positional cloning relies on segregation (Mendelian) and linkage analysis. Given the numerous limitations associated with such analyses in human populations (family and sample size, *etc.*) it is unlikely that this technique will be successfully applied to genetically complex traits in the near future.

7. Even though you have developed a method for screening seven of the mutations described, it is possible that negative results can occur even though the person carries the gene for CF. In other words, the specific probes (or allele-specific oligonucleotides) that have been developed will not necessarily be useful for screening all mutant genes. In addition, the cost-effectiveness of such a screening proposal would need to be considered.

8. It will hybridize to the normal DNA sequence because it is fully complementary to the bottom normal strand.

9. In the case of haplo-insufficient mutations, gene therapy holds promise; however in "gain-of-function" mutations in all probability, the mutant gene's activity or product must be compromised. It is possible to introduce antisenst RNA or DNA that will base pair with the mutant RNA and compromise its influence. Addition of a normal gene probably will not help.

10. The answer provided here is based on the condition that individual I-2 is a carrier and the son, II-4, has the disorder. The 3kb fragment occurs in the normal I-1 father and the normal son II-1. The affected son, II-4, has the 4kb fragment. One daughter, II-2, is a carrier while the other daughter, II-3, is not a carrier.

11. One method is to use the amino acid sequence of the protein to produce the gene synthetically. Alternatively, since the introns are spliced out of the hnRNA in the production of mRNA, if mRNA can be obtained, it can be used to make cDNA through the use of reverse transcriptase.

12. The two major problems described here are common concerns related to genetic engineering. The first is the localization of the introduced DNA into the target tissue and target location in the genome. Inappropriate targeting may have serious consequences. In addition, it is often difficult to control the output of introduced DNA. Genetic regulation is complicated and subject to a number of factors including upstream and downstream signals as well as various posttranscriptional processing schemes. Artificial control of these factors will prove difficult.

Chapter 20: Genes and Development

Concept Areas	Corresponding Problems
Developmental Concepts	1, 9
Variable Gene Activity Theory	4
Differential Transcription in Development	3, 5
Genetics of Embryonic Deveopment	2, 6, 8
Homeotic Genes	7

Vocabulary and Critical Issues

Structures and Substances

Zygote

Drosophila

   molecular gradient

   syncytial blastoderm

   pol plasm

   cellular blastoderm

   compartment

   imaginal discs

   eyeless

   Small eye

   maternal effect genes

   zygotic genes

   segmentation genes

     gap genes

     pair-rule genes

     segment polarity genes

selector genes

homeotic genes

   antennapedia complex

   bithorax complex

   homeobox, homeodomain

   Hox gene clusters

Arabidopsis

   MADS-box proteins

Caenorhabditis elegans

   male, hermaphrodite

   lin, let, etc.

   vulva

Molecular gradients

   anterior-posterior axis

   maternal-effect genes

Maternal cytoplasm

Blastoderm

Chapter 20

Processes/Methods

Development

  cytoplasmic localization

  cell-cell interaction

  determination

    selective expression

    regulatory events

    patterns of gene activity

      cascades

      muscle cell development

    multistep

    progressive restriction

  differentiation

    genetic and morphological changes

  cell-cell interaction

    vulval formation

Analyses

  Drosophila

    oogenesis

    syncytial cellular blastoderm

    imaginal disks

molecular gradients

  anterior-posterior

  dorsal-ventral

segmentation

selector genes

  homeotic mutants

C. elegans

Concepts

Development (F20.1)

  variable gene activity (F20.2)

  eukaryotes

    determination

    differentiation

    cell-cell interaction

  Maternal influences

  anterior-posterior gradient

  positional information

Cytoplasmic influences

Homeotic genes

Homeodomains

F20.1. Illustration of the relationship between *determination* and *differentiation*. Determination sets the program which will later be revealed during differentiation.

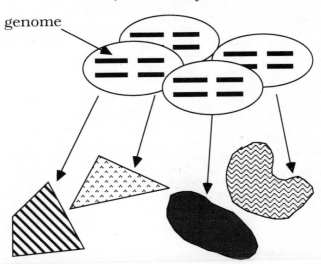

Cells become DETERMINED
(structurally uniform)

genome

Cells DIFFERENTIATE
(structurally different)

F20.2. Illustration of the genomic changes which are thought to occur during cell differentiation. T[ ]
variable gene activity model states that different sets of genes are transcriptionally active in differen[ ]
ated cells.

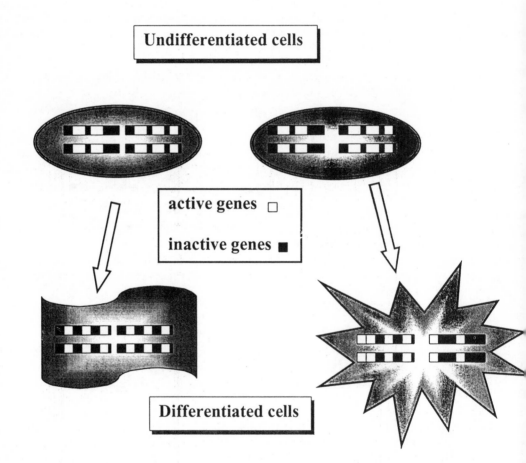

Solutions to Problems
and Discussion Questions

1. *Determination* refers to early developmental and regulatory events which set eventual patterns of gene activity. Determination is not the end result of the regulatory activity, rather, it is the process by which the developmental fate of a particular cell type is fixed. *Differentiation* on the other hand follows determination and is the manifestation, in terms of genetic, physiological, and morphological changes, of the determined state.

2. Many of the appendages of the head, including the mouth parts and the antennae are evolutionary derivatives of ancestral leg structures. In *spineless aristapedia* the distal portion of the antenna is replaced by its ancestral counterpart, the distal portion of the leg (tarsal segments). Because the replacement of the arista (end of the antenna) can occur by a mutation in a single gene, one would consider that one "selector" gene distinguishes aristal from tarsal structures. Notice that a "one-step" change is involved in the interchange of leg and antennal structures.

3. Actinomycin D is useful in determining the involvement of transcription on molecular and developmental processes. Because maternal RNAs are present in the fertilized sea urchin egg (as is the case with many egg types) a considerable amount of development can occur without transcription. Because gastrulation is inhibited by *prior* treatment with actinomycin D, it would appear that earlier gene products are necessary for the initiation and/or continuation of gastrulation. Clearly a critical period (6th to 11th hours of development) exists for gastrulation in which gene activity is required.

4. There are several somewhat indirect methods for determining transcriptional activity of a given gene in different cell types. First, if protein products of a given gene are present in different cell types, it can be assumed that the responsible gene is being transcribed. Second, if one is able to actually observe, microscopically, gene activity, as is the case in some specialized chromosomes (polytene chromosomes), gene activity can be inferred by the presence of localized chromosomal puffs.

A more direct and common practice to assess transcription of particular genes is to use labeled probes. If a labeled probe can be obtained which contains base sequences that are complementary to the transcribed RNA, then such probes will hybridize to that RNA if present in different tissues. This technique is called *in situ* hybridization and is a powerful tool in the study of gene activity during development.

5. There are a variety of approaches to determine the level of control of a particular gene. First, one may determine whether levels of hnRNA are consistent among various cell types of interest. This is often accomplished by either direct isolation of the RNA and assessment by northern blotting or by use of *in situ* hybridization. If the hnRNA pools for a given gene are consistent in various cell types, then transcriptional control can be eliminated as a possibility. Support for translational control can be achieved directly by determining, in different cell types, the presence of a variety of mRNA species with common sequences. This can be accomplished only in cases where sufficient knowledge exists for specific mRNA trapping or labeling. Clues as to translational control *via* alternative splicing can sometimes be achieved by examining the amino acid sequence of proteins. Similarities in certain structural/functional motifs may indicate alternative RNA processing.

6. Because in *ftz/ftz* embryos, the engrailed product is absent and in *en/en* embryos *ftz* expression is normal, one can conclude that the *ftz* gene product regulates, either directly or indirectly, *en*.

7. A *homeotic mutant* alters the identity of a segment or field within a segment as if it were another segment or field. While homologies do exist between widely diverse groups, some differences in function have evolved. It is likely that functional overlap would not occur, however, only an actual experiment would answer the question.

8. The fact that nuclei from almost any source remain transcriptionally and translationally active substantiates the fact that the genetic code and the ancillary processes of transcription and translation are compatible throughout the animal and plant kingdoms. Because the egg represents an isolated, "closed" system which can be mechanically, environmentally, and to some extent biochemically manipulated, various conditions may be developed which allow one to study facets of gene regulation. For instance, the influence of transcriptional enhancers and suppressors may be studied along with factors which impact on translational and post-translational processes. Combinations of injected nuclei may reveal nuclear-nuclear interactions which could not normally be studied by other methods.

9. The egg is not an unorganized collection of molecules from which life springs after fertilization. It is a highly organized structure, "preformed" in the sense that maternal informational molecules are oriented to provide an anterior-posterior and dorsal-ventral pattern from which nuclei receive positional cues. Such positional cues lead to the "determined" state, from which cells later reveal their adult form (differentiation).

Indeed, in *Drosophila* and many other organisms, embryonic fate maps may be constructed thereby attesting to the maternally-derived "prepattern" present in the egg. The egg therefore *is* preformed, not in the sense that a miniature individual resides, but in a molecular prepattern upon which development depends. However, work by Spemann, Briggs and King, and Gurdon, indicates that there is plasticity in the programming of nuclei and that even nuclei from somewhat specialized cells often have the potential to direct the development of the entire adult individual. Such is the case with the more recent cloning of Dolly, a mammal. Such *totipotent* behavior of cells indicates that development arises as a result of a series of progressive steps in which cells acquire new structures and functions as development progresses. The epigenetic theory as viewed today is the result of sequential, differential gene expression.

Chapter 21: The Genetic Basis of Cancer

Concept Areas

Vocabulary and Critical Issues

Structures and Substances

Cancer susceptibility genes

Carcinogen

Saccharomyces cerevisiae

Schizosaccharomyces pombe

    G 1, G2, S, G0

    checkpoints

  protein kinases

    cyclin-dependent kinase

    CDK1, CDK4, cdc2

  cyclins (A, B, C, D1, D2, E)

  CDK1/cyclin B

  G1 checkpoint, M checkpoint

Tumor suppressor genes

  pRB

  RB, E2F

  proto-oncogenes (*c-onc*)

oncogenes (*onc*)

  v-onc, c-src, other oncogenes, *ras*, etc.

  point mutation

  translocation

  overexpression

BRCA1 (chromosome 17)

BRCA2 (chromosome 13)

  dominant genes

Chk2

Sarcoma

  retrovirus, Rous sarcoma virus

    reverse transcriptase

  provirus

    acute transforming virus

    nonacute (nondefective) virus

p53, "guardian of the genome"

   p21

   gatekeeper genes

   caretaker genes

polyp

Processes/Methods

Metastasis

Cell cycle control

CDK/Cyclin complex phosphorylation

Cancer

   chromosomal changes

      loss, rearrangement, insertions

      chronic myeloid leukemia (CML)

      Philadelphia chromosome

   hybrid genes, hybrid proteins

   lymphoma

Environmental factors

hepatocellular carcinoma

hepatitis B virus

   CCNA2

   ionizing radiation

   chemicals

   diet, drugs

   ultraviolet light

Genetic predisposition

   retinoblastoma

   autosomal dominant, 90% "penetrant"

      familial, sporatic

      phosphorylation, dephosphorylation

Apoptosis

   colon cancer

   hereditary nonpolyposis colorectal cancer (HNPCC)

      2p16, 3p21

      MSH2

      MLH1

   familial adenomatous polyposis (FAP)

   APC, DCC, p53, sequential aspects

Concepts

Cellular basis of cancer (genetic involvement)

   somatic *versus* germline

Genetic influences, instability

   suppressor genes

   oncogenes, protooncogenes

Model for retinoblastoma control

Origin of oncogenes

Environmental involvement

Solutions to Problems and Discussion Questions

1. Familial retinoblastoma is inherited as an autosomal dominant gene with 90% penetrance, that is, 90% of the individuals which inherit the gene will develop eye tumors. The gene usually expresses itself in youngsters. Because the husband's sister has RB, one of the husband's parents has the gene for RB and the husband has a 50:50 chance of inheriting that gene. However, because the husband is past the usual age of onset, it is quite likely that he was lucky and did not receive the RB gene. In that case, the chance that a child born to this couple having RB is no higher than the frequency of sporatic occurrence. However, because the gene is 90% penetrant, there is a chance that the husband has the gene but does not express it. The probability of that occurrence would be 0.50 (of inheriting the gene) X 0.10 (not expressing the gene) = 0.05. The chance of the husband then passing this non-expressed gene to his child would be again 0.5, so 0.50 X 0.05 = 0.025 for the child inheriting this gene. If the child inherits the RB gene, he/she has a 90% chance of expressing it. Therefore the overall probability of the child having RB (using this logic) would be 0.025 X 0.9 = 0.0225 or just over 2% (or about 1 in 50).

To test the presence of the RB gene in the husband, it is possible in some forms of RB to identify (by Southern blot) a defective or missing DNA segment. Otherwise, one might attempt to assay the RB product in cells to see if it is present and functional at normal levels.

2. Review Chapter 2 in the text and note that the following stages of the cell cycle are discussed: G1, G0, S, G2. The G1 stage begins after mitosis and is involved in the synthesis of many cytoplasmic elements. In the S phase DNA synthesis occurs. G2 is a period of growth and preparation for mitosis. Most cell cycle time variation is caused by changes in the duration of G1. G0 is the non-dividing state.

3. The major regulatory points of the cell cycle include the following:

1. Late G1 (G1/S)
2. The border between G2 and mitosis (G2/M)
3. In mitosis (M)

4. Kinases regulate other proteins by adding phosphate groups. Cyclins bind to the kinases, switching them on and off. Several cyclins, including D and E, can move cells from G1 to S. At the G2/mitosis border a CDK1 (cyclin dependent kinase) combines with another cyclin (cyclin B). Phosphorylation occurs bringing about a series of changes in the nuclear membrane, cytoskeleton, and histone 1.

5. To say that a particular trait is inherited conveys the assumption that when a particular genetic circumstance is present, it will be revealed in the phenotype. For instance, albinism is inherited in such a way that individuals who are homozygous recessive, express albinism. When one discusses an inherited predisposition, one usually refers to situations where a particular phenotype is expressed in families in some consistent pattern. However, the phenotype may not always be expressed or may manifest itself in different ways. In retinoblastoma, the gene is inherited as an autosomal dominant and those that inherit the mutant RB allele are predisposed to develop eye tumors. However, approximately 10% of the people known to inherit the gene don't actually express it and in some cases expression involves only one eye rather than two.

6. A tumor suppressor gene is a gene that normally functions to suppress cell division. Since tumors and cancers represent a significant threat to survival and therefore Darwinian fitness, strong evolutionary forces would favor a variety of co-evolved and perhaps complex conditions in which mutations in these suppressor genes would be recessive. Looking at it in another way, if a tumor suppressor gene makes a product that regulates the cell cycle favorably, cellular conditions have evolved in such a way that sufficient quantities of this gene product are made from just one gene (of the two present in each diploid individual) to provide normal function.

7. Oncogenes are genes that induce or maintain uncontrolled cellular proliferation associated with cancer. They are mutant forms of proto-oncogenes which normally function to regulate cell division. Alterations may be in the form of point mutations, gene amplification, translocation, changes in regulatory sequences, *etc.*

8. A translocation involving exchange of genetic material between chromosomes 9 and 22 is responsible for the generation of the "Philadelphia chromosome." Genetic mapping established that certain oncogenes were combined to form a hybrid gene that encodes a 200kd protein which has been implicated in the formation of chronic myelocytic leukemia.

9. Unfortunately, it is common to spend enormous amounts of money on dealing with diseases after they occur rather than concentrating on disease prevention. Too often pressure from special interest groups or lack of political stimulus retards advances in education and prevention. Obviously, it is less expensive, both in terms of human suffering and money, to seek preventive measures for as many diseases as possible. However, having gained some understanding of the mechanisms of disease, in this case cancer, it must also be stated that no matter what preventive measures are taken it will be impossible to completely eliminate disease from the human population. It is extremely important, however, that we increase efforts to educate and protect the human population from as many hazardous environmental agents as possible.

10. Any agent which causes damage to DNA is a potential carcinogen since cell cycle control is achieved by gene (DNA) products, known as proteins. Since cigarette smoke is known to contain an agent which changes DNA, in this case transversions, numerous modified gene products (including cell cycle controlling proteins) are likely to be produced. The fact that many cancer patients have such transversions in *p53* strongly suggests that cancer is caused by agents in cigarette smoke.

Chapter 22: Population Genetics

Concept Areas	Corresponding Problems
Calculating Allele Frequencies	1, 2
The Hardy-Weinberg Law	3, 4, 6, 9, 10, 18
Extensions of the Hardy-Weinberg Law	19
Using the Hardy-Weinberg Law	5, 7, 8, 9, 11, 17
Factors that Alter Allele Frequencies	12, 13, 14, 15, 16

Vocabulary and Critical Issues

Historical

Wallace- Darwin

The Origin of Species (1859)

Hardy - Weinberg

Structures and Substances

Population

gene pool

CC-CKR-S

Processes/Methods

Allele frequencies

mutation

rates

dwarfism

achondroplasia

migration

selection

fitness

selection coefficient

directional

stabilizing

heterozygote superiority

disruptive

genetic drift

achromatopsia

Symbolism

p, q

$p + q = 1$

$p^2 + 2pq + q^2 = 1$

Multiple alleles

$p + q + r = 1$

$p^2 + 2pq + 2pr + q^2 + 2qr + r^2 = 1$

Heterozygote frequency

$$\sqrt{q^2}$$

$p = 1 - q$

$2pq$

Inbreeding and hybrid vigor

    inbreeding

        self-fertilization

        consanguineous marriages

        coefficient of inbreeding

        inbreeding depression

          hybrid vigor (F22.2)

            dominance hypothesis

            overdominance

Concepts

    Population genetics

    Gene pool

        allelic frequencies (F22.1)

    Hardy-Weinberg law

        assumptions

        infinitely large

          no genetic drift

        random mating

        no selection

        no mutation

        no migration

    Genetic equilibrium

        genetic variety and endangered species

    Inbreeding and hybrid vigor (F22.2)

F22.1. Diagram of the relationships among populations, individuals, alleles, and allelic frequencies (p, q).

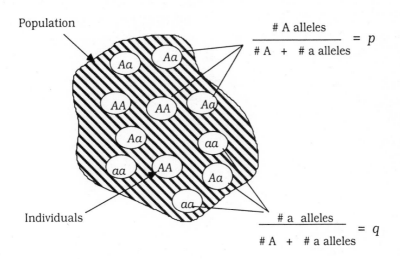

F22.2. Diagram of the relationships among inbreeding, heterosis, and homozygosity. Note that as inbreeding occurs, heterosis decreases while homozygosity increases.

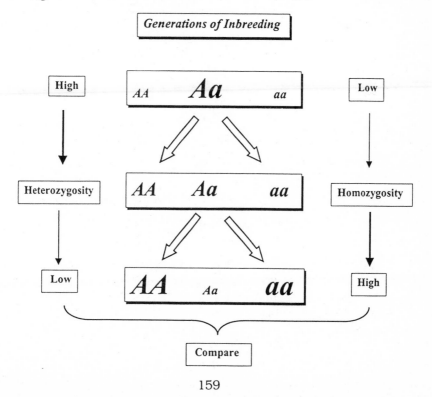

Solutions to Problems
and Discussion Questions

1. Because the alleles follow a dominant/recessive mode, one can use the equation $\sqrt{q^2}$ to calculate q from which all other aspects of the answer depend. The frequency of aa types is determined by dividing 37 (number of non-tasters) by the total number of individuals (125).

$$q^2 = 37/125 = .296$$

$$q = .544$$

$$p = 1 - q$$

$$p = .456$$

The frequencies of the genotypes are determined by applying the formula $p^2 + 2pq + q^2$ as follows:

Frequency of AA = p^2

= $(.456)^2$

= .208 or 20.8%

Frequency of Aa = $2pq$

= $2(.456)(.544)$

= .496 or 49.6%

Frequency of aa = q^2

= $(.544)^2$

= .296 or 29.6%

When completing such a set of calculations it is a good practice to add the final percentages to be certain that they total 100%.

2. Understanding the Hardy-Weinberg equilibrium allows us to state that if a population is equilibrium, the genotypic frequencies will not shift from one generation to the next unless there are factors such as selection, migration, etc. which alter gene frequencies. Since none of these factors are stated in the problem, we need only to determine whether the initial population is in equilibrium. Calculate p and q, then apply the equation $p^2 + 2pq + q^2$ to determine genotypic frequencies in the next generation.

p = frequency of A

= 0.2 + .3

= 0.5

q = $1 - p$ = 0.5

Frequency of AA = p^2

= $(.5)^2$

= .25 or 25%

Frequency of Aa = $2pq$

= $2(.5)(.5)$

= .5 or 50%

Frequency of aa = q^2

= $(.5)^2$

= .25 or 25%

The initial population was not in equilibrium, however, after one generation of mating under the Hardy-Weinberg assumptions, the population is in equilibrium and will continue to be so (and not change) until one or more of the Hardy-Weinberg assumptions is not met. Note that *equilibrium* does not necessarily mean p and q equal 0.5.

3. For each of these values, one merely takes the square root to determine q, then one computes p, then one "plugs" the values into the $2pq$ expression.

(a) $q = .08$; $2pq = 2(.92)(.08)$

$\qquad = .1472$ or 14.72%

(b) $q = .009$; $2pq = 2(.991)(.009)$

$\qquad = .01784$ or 1.78%

(c) $q = .3$; $2pq = 2(.7)(.3)$

$\qquad = .42$ or 42%

(d) $q = .1$; $2pq = 2(.9)(.1)$

$\qquad = .18$ or 18%

(e) $q = .316$; $2pq = 2(.684)(.316)$

$\qquad = .4323$ or 43.23%

(depending how one rounds off the decimals, slightly different answers will occur)

4. In order for the Hardy-Weinberg equations to apply, the population must be in equilibrium.

5. If one has the frequency of individuals with the dominant phenotype, the remainder have the recessive phenotype (q^2). With q^2 one can calculate q and from this value one can arrive at p. Applying the expression $p^2 + 2pq + q^2$ will allow a solution to the question.

6. (a) For the CCR5 analysis, first determine p and q. Since one has the frequencies of all the genotypes, one can add

.6 and .351/2 to provide p (= .7755);

q will be

1 - .7755 or .2245.

The equilibrium values will be as follows:

Frequency of $1/1$ $\quad = \quad p^2 = \quad (.7755)^2$

$\qquad = .6014$ or 60.14%

Frequency of $1/\Delta 32$ $\quad = \quad 2pq$

$\qquad = 2(.7755)(.2245)$

$\qquad = .3482$ or 34.82%

Frequency of $\Delta 32/\Delta 32$ $\quad = \quad q^2 = \quad (.2245)^2$

$\qquad = .0504$ or 5.04%

Comparing these equilibrium values with the observed values strongly suggests that the observed values are drawn from a population in equilibrium.

(b) For the AS analysis, first determine p and q. Since one has the frequencies of all the genotypes, one can add

.756 and .242/2 to provide p (= .877);

q will be

1 - .877 or .123.

The equilibrium values will be as follows:

Frequency of AA $\quad = \quad p^2 = \quad (.877)^2$

$\qquad = .7691$ or 76.91%

Frequency of AS $\quad = \quad 2pq = 2(.877)(.123)$

$\qquad = .2157$ or 21.57%

Frequency of SS $\quad = \quad q^2 = \quad (.123)^2$

$\qquad = .0151$ or 1.51%

Comparing these equilibrium values with the observed values suggests that the observed values may be drawn from a population which is not in equilibrium. Notice that there are more heterozygotes than predicted, and fewer SS types. To test for a Hardy-Weinberg equilibrium, apply the chi-square test as follows.

$$\chi^2 = \frac{\Sigma (o-e)^2}{e}$$

$(75.6-76.9)^2/76.9 \; +$

$(24.2 - 21.6)^2/21.6 \; +$

$(0.2 - 1.51)^2/1.5 \quad = \quad 1.47$

In calculating degrees of freedom in a test of gene frequencies, the "free variables" are reduced by an additional degree of freedom because one estimated a parameter (p or q) used in determining the expected values. Therefore, there is one degree of freedom even though there are three classes. Checking the χ^2 table with 1 degree of freedom gives a value of 3.84 at the 0.05 probability level. Since the χ^2 value calculated here is smaller, the null hypothesis (the observed values fluctuate from the equilibrium values by chance and chance alone) should not be rejected. Thus the frequencies of AA, AS, SS sampled a population which is in equilibrium.

7. Given that $q^2 = .04$, then $q = .2$, $2pq = .32$, and $p^2 = .64$. Of those not expressing the trait, only a mating between heterozygotes can produce an offspring which expresses the trait, and then only at a frequency of $1/4$. The different types of matings possible (those without the trait) in the population, with their frequencies, are given below:

$AA \; X \; AA \; = \; .64 \; X \; .64 \; = \; .4096$

$AA \; X \; Aa \; = \; .64 \; X \; .32 \; = \; .2048$

$Aa \; X \; AA \; = \; .64 \; X \; .32 \; = \; .2048$

$Aa \; X \; Aa \; = \; .32 \; X \; .32 \; = \; .1024$

$Aa \; X \; Aa \; = \; .32 \; X \; .32 \; = \; .1024$

Notice that of the matings of the individuals who do not express the trait, only the last two (about 20%) are capable of producing offspring with the trait. Therefor, one would arrive at a final likelihood of $1/4$ X 20% or 5% of the offspring with the trait.

8. The following formula calculates the frequency of an allele in the next generation for any selection scenario, given the frequencies of a and A in this generation and the fitness of all three genotypes:

$$q_{g+1} = [w_{Aa}p_g q_g + w_{aa}q_g^2]/[w_{AA}p_g^2 + w_{Aa}2p_g q_g + w_{aa}q_g^2]$$

where q_{g+1} is the frequency of the a allele in the next generation, q_g is the frequency of the a allele in this generation, p_g is the frequenc of the A allele in this generation, and each "w" represents the fitness of their respective genotypes.

(a)

$$q_{g+1} = [.9(.7)(.3) + .8(.3)^2/[1(.7)^2 + .9(2)(.7)(.3) + .8(.3)^2]$$

q_{g+1}	= .278
p_{g+1}	= .722

(b)

q_{g+1}	= .289
p_{g+1}	= .711

(c)

q_{g+1}	= .298
p_{g+1}	= .702

(d)

q_{g+1}	= .319
p_{g+1}	= .681

9. The general equation for responding to this question is

$$q_n = q_o/(1 + nq_o)$$

where n = the number of generations, q_o = the initial gene frequency, and q_n = the new gene frequency.

(a)

$q_n = q_o/(1 + nq_o)$

$q_n = 0.5 / [1 + (1 \; X \; 0.5)]$

$q_n = .33 \quad p_n = .67$

(b)

$$q_n = q_o /(1 + nq_o)$$

$$q_n = 0.5 / [1 + (5 \ X \ 0.5)]$$

$$q_n = .143 \qquad p_n = .857$$

(c)

$$q_n = q_o /(1 + nq_o)$$

$$q_n = 0.5 / [1 + (10 \ X \ 0.5)]$$

$$q_n = .083 \qquad p_n = .917$$

(d)

$$q_n = q_o /(1 + nq_o)$$

$$q_n = 0.5 / [1 + (25 \ X \ 0.5)]$$

$$q_n = .037 \qquad p_n = .963$$

(e)

$$q_n = q_o /(1 + nq_o)$$

$$q_n = 0.5 / [1 + (100 \ X \ 0.5)]$$

$$q_n = .0098 \qquad p_n = .9902$$

(f)

$$q_n = q_o /(1 + nq_o)$$

$$q_n = 0.5 / [1 + (1000 \ X \ 0.5)]$$

$$q_n = .00099 \qquad p_n = .99901$$

10. For this question, apply the equations

$$\Delta p = m(p_m - p)$$

and $p_l = p + \Delta p.$

Substituting, gives: $p_l = p + m(p_m - p).$

(a) $p_l = 0.6 + 0.2(0.1 - 0.6) = 0.5$

(b) $p_l = 0.2 + 0.3(0.7 - 0.2) = 0.35$

(c) $p_l = 0.1 + 0.1(0.2 - 0.1) = 0.11$

11. What one must do is predict the probability of one of the grandparents being heterozygous in this problem. Given the frequency of the disorder in the population as 1 in 10,000 individuals (0.0001), then $q^2 = 0.0001$, and $q = 0.01$. The frequency of heterozygosity is $2pq$ or approximately .02 as also stated in the problem. The probability for one of the grandparents to be heterozygous would therefore be 0.02 + 0.02 or 0.04 or 1/25.

If one of the grandparents is a carrier, then the probability of the offspring from a first-cousin mating being homozygous for the recessive gene is 1/16. Multiplying the two probabilities together gives 1/16 X 1/25 = 1/400. Inbreeding therefore increases the likelihood of homozygosity by a factor of about 25.

12. *Inbreeding depression* refers to the reduction in fitness observed in populations which are inbred. With inbreeding comes an increase in the number of homozygous individuals (see F22.2 in this book) and a decrease in genetic variability. Genetic variability is necessary for a genetic response to environmental change. As deleterious genes become homozygous, more individuals are less fit in the population.

13. Because heterozygosity tends to mask expression of recessive genes which may be desirable in a domesticated animal or plant, inbreeding schemes will often be used to render strains homozygous so that such recessive genes can be expressed.

In addition, assume that a particularly desirable trait occurs in a domesticated plant or animal. The best way to increase the frequency of individuals with that trait is by self-fertilization (not often possible) or by matings to blood relatives (inbreeding). In theory, one increases the likelihood of a gene "meeting itself" by various inbreeding schemes. There are disadvantages to increasing the degree of homozygosity by inbreeding. *Inbreeding depression* is a reduction in fitness often associated with an increase in homozygosity.

14. While inbreeding increases the frequency of homozygous individuals in a population, it does not change the *allele* frequencies. There will be fewer heterozygotes in the population to compensate for the additional homozygotes. See F22.2 in this book.

15. The quickest way to generate a homozygous line of an organism is to *self-fertilize* that organism. Because this is not always possible, brother-sister matings, or matings between other relatives are often used. Indeed, matings between offspring and their parents are also useful in rendering some organisms homozygous for desired traits.

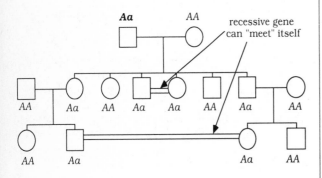

16. Given that the recessive gene a is present in the homozygous state (q^2) at a frequency of 0.0001, the value of q is 0.01 and $p = 0.99$.

(a) q is 0.01

(b) $p = 1 - q$ or .99

(c) $2pq = 2(.01)(.99)$
$= 0.0198$ (or about 1/50)

(d) $2pq \times 2pq$

$= 0.0198 \times 0.0198$
$= 0.000392$ or about 1/255

17. The frequency of a gene is determined by a number of factors, including the fitness it confers, mutation rate, and input from migration. There is no tendency for a gene to reach any artificial frequency such as 0.5. The distribution of a gene among individuals is determined by mating (population size, inbreeding, etc.) and environmental factors (selection, etc.). A population is in equilibrium when the distribution of genotypes occurs at or around the $p^2 + 2pq + q^2$ expression.

Equilibrium does not mean 25% *AA*, 50% *Aa*, and 25% *aa*. This confusion often stems from the 1:2:1 (or 3:1) ratio seen in Mendelian crosses.

18. Because three of the affected infants had affected parents, only two "new" genes, from mutation, enter into the problem. The gene is dominant, therefore each new case of achondroplasia arose from a single new mutation. There are 50,000 births, therefore 100,000 genes (gametes) involved. The frequency of mutation is therefore given as follows:

2/100,000

or 2×10^{-5}

19. The probability that the woman (with no family history of CF) is heterozygous is $2pq$ or $2(1/50)(49/50)$. The probability that the man is heterozygous is 2/3. The probability that a child with CF will be produced by two heterozygotes is 1/4. Therefore, the overall probability of the couple producing a CF child is 98/2500 $\times$ 2/3 $\times$ 1/4.

Chapter 23: Genetics and Evolution

Concept Areas	Corresponding Problems
Chromosomal Polymorphism	1
Models of Speciation	2
Formation of Species	10
Using Molecular Techniques to Study Evolution	3, 4, 5, 6, 7, 8, 9, 11

Vocabulary and Critical Issues

Structures and Substances

Niche

Species

Phylogeny

Origin of Species (1859)

Allozyme

    alcohol dehydrogenase

    cystic fibrosis transmembrane conductance regulator (CFTR)

Cytochrome c

Drosophila pseudoobscura

    polytene chromosome

    inversion polymorphisms

    starch-adapted

    maltose-adapted

Fundulus heroclitus (mummichog)

    lactate dehydrogenase

    ectotherm

Snapping shrimp

    Mimulus cardinalis

    Mimulus lewisii

Chichlids

    SINES

Evolutionary tree

    Homo neanderthalensis

    Homo sapiens

Mitochondrial DNA

    SSU rRNA

Processes/Methods

Phyletic evolution

    anagenesis, cladogenesis

Evolutionary divergence (F23.1)

    variation

    overpopulation

    struggle for survival

    differential survival

    species formation

Genetic diversity

    heterozygosity

        protein polymorphism

        allozymes (F23.1)

            nucleotide sequence

            molecular phylogenetic trees

    amino acid sequence homology

        cytochrome c

    chromosomal polymorphism

        inversions, translocations

    DNA sequence polymorphism

        mitochondrial DNA

Ecological diversity

    niche

Speciation

    allopolyploidy

    stasis

    phyletic evolution (anagenesis)

    cladogenesis

    neutralist theory

    selectionist theory

    reproductive barriers

        physiological

        behavioral

        mechanical

    reproductive isolating mechanisms

        prezygotic, postzygotic

Gel electrophoresis

    protein polymorphism

    nucleic acid sequence variation

UPGMA

HIV transmission

Concepts

Niche

Evolutionary divergence

    molecular clock

    minimal mutational distance

    minimal genetic divergence

    rates of speciation

    divergence dendrograms

    evolutionary trees

Species formation (speciation)

Phylogenetic reconstruction

Sequence homology

    amino acid, nucleic acid

Sequence conservation

Parsimony

Maximum likelihood

Mutation and speciation

    neutralist theory

        functional constraints (F23.2)

        cost of selection

    selectionists hypothesis

F23.1. The diagram below is meant to illustrate the meaning of the term *allozyme*. Notice that alleles, genes *A'* and *A''*, produce protein products which differ electrophoretically but are involved in the same function.

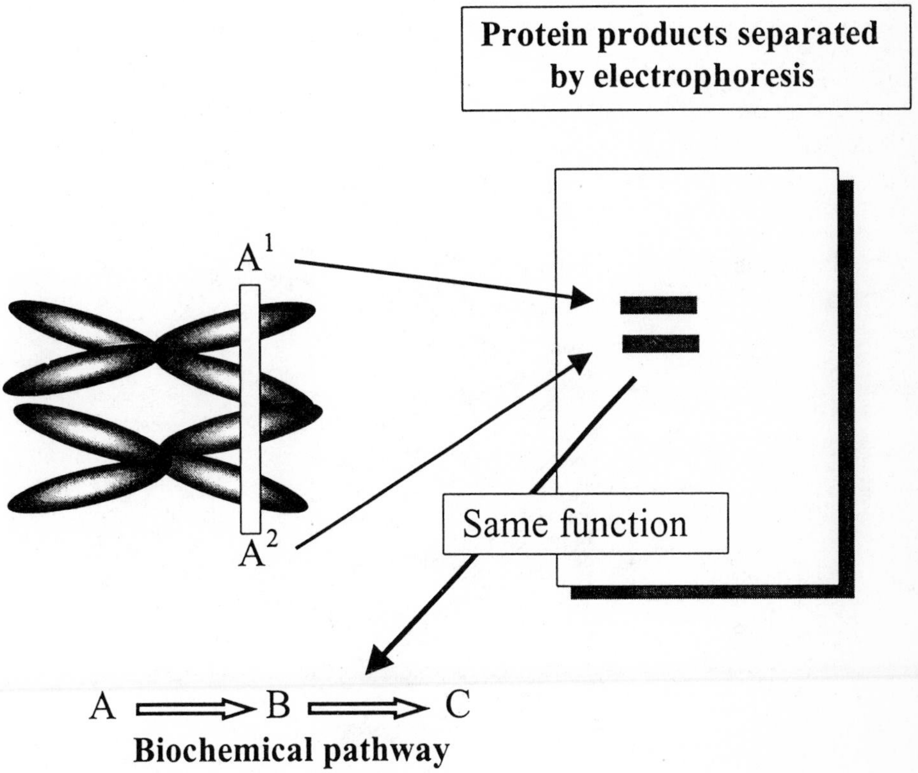

Protein products separated by electrophoresis

A^1

A^2

Same function

A ⟹ B ⟹ C
Biochemical pathway

F23.2. The illustration below is meant to show that certain parts of the protein would be more able to withstand changes in amino acid sequence than those with functional constraints. Those areas most distant from the "functional portions" would seem to be more tolerant to change.

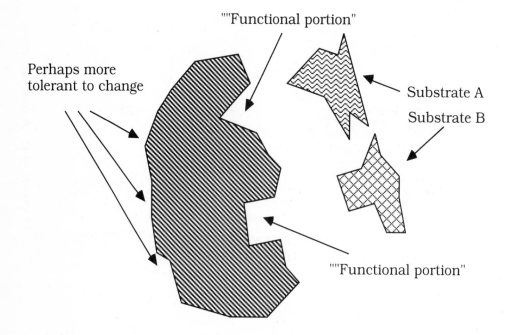

Solutions to Problems and Discussion Questions

1. Assume that a chromosome in the "standard arrangement" undergoes an inversion (pericentric or paracentric). The following are possible consequences of such an inversion:

(a) change in gene order with possible introduction of position effects,

(b) breakage within a structural gene or other functional element,

(c) reduction in the recovery of crossover gametes in heterokaryotypes (those which carry an inversion as well as a standard homologue). While "c" may reduce the production of variation, the first two (a and b) may introduce variation.

At the populationa level, ifferent populations with different inversion polymorphisms are genetically distinct.

2. During speciation individuals or groups of potentially interbreeding organisms become genetically distinct from other members of the species. Members of different populations with substantial genetic divergence are, at first, not reproductively isolated from each other although gene flow may be restricted. The distinction between such groups is not absolute in that one group may blend with other groups of the species. Any process which favors changes in gene frequencies has the potential of generating substantial genetic differences.

Factors such as selection, migration, genetic drift, or even mutation, may be important in generating genetic change. One would certainly include geographic isolation as a major barrier to gene flow and thus an important process in such formation.

Natural selection occurs when there is non-random elimination of individuals from a population. Since such selection is a strong force in changing gene frequencies, it should also be considered as a significant factor in generating genetic variation amoung populations.

3. Because of degeneracy in the code, there are some nucleotide substitutions, especially in the third base, which do not change amino acids. In addition, if there is no change in the overall charge of the protein, it is likely that electrophoresis will not separate the variants. If a positively charged amino acid is replaced by an amino acid of like charge, then the overall charge on the protein is unchanged. The same may be said for other, negatively charged and neutral amino acid substitutions.

4. All of the amino acid substitutions

(Ala -> Gly, Val -> Leu, Asp -> Asn, Met -> Leu)

require only one nucleotide change. The last change from

    Pro (CC-) -> Lys (AAA,G)

requires two changes (the minimal mutational distance).

5. Approach this problem by writing the possible codons for all the amino acids (except Arg and Asp which show no change) in the human cytochrome c chain. Then determine the minimum number of nucleotide substitutions required for each changed amino acid in the various organisms. Once listed, then count up the numbers for each organism: horse, 3; pig, 2; dog, 3; chicken, 3; bullfrog, 2; fungus, 6.

6. Construct a chart similar to the one below which indicates the number of base changes between each pair:

	H	C	G	O
H	-	-	-	-
C	1	-	-	-
G	3	2	-	-
O	7	6	4	-
B	12	11	9	10

Generate the first cluster by selecting the closest related pair (human and chimp). Considering the human-chimp cluster as one entity, "average" its (human and chimp) distance to the next closest primate (gorilla). Continue to treat each new cluster (human-chimp-gorilla) as a single entity, comparing it to the next closest organism until all the ogranisms are exhausted. Construct the tree on the basis of the average mutational distances as described in the text.

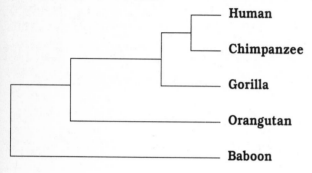

7. The classification of organisms into different species is based on evidence (morphological, genetic, ecological, etc.) that they are reproductively isolated. That is, there must be evidence that gene flow does not occur among the groups being called different species. Classifications above the species level (genus, family, etc.) are not based on such empirical data. Indeed, classification above the species level is somewhat arbitrary and based on traditions which extend far beyond DNA sequence information.

In addition, recall that DNA sequence divergence is not always directly proportional to morphological, behavioral, or ecological divergence. Therefore, while the genus classifications provided in this problem seem to be invalid, other factors, well beyond simple DNA sequence comparison, must be considered in classification practices. As more information is gained on the meaning of DNA sequence differences (ΔT_m) in comparison to morphological factors, many phylogenetic relationships will be reconsidered and it is possible that adjustments will be needed in some classification schemes.

8. In looking at the figure, notice that the $\Delta T_{50}H$ value of 4.0 on the right could be used as a decision point such that any group which diverged above that line would be considered in the same genus while any group below would be in a different genus. Under this rule, one would have the chimpanzee, pygmy chimpanzee, human, gorilla and orangutan in the same genus. If one assumed that 3.7 is close enough to be considered above 4.0, given considerable experimental error, one could provide a scheme where the orangutan is not included with the chimpanzee, pygmy chimpanzee, human, and gorilla.

9. There are many sections of DNA in a eukaryotic genome which are not reflected in a protein product. Indeed, there are many sections of DNA which are not even transcribed and/or have no apparent physiological role. Such regions are more likely to tolerate nucleotide changes compared to those regions with a necessary physiological impact. Introns for example show sequence variation which is not reflected in a protein product. Exons on the other hand code for products which are usually involved in production of a phenotype and as such are subject to selection.

10. The text lists several cornerstones of the *neutral mutation theory*:

(a) the relatively uniform rate of amino acid substitution in different organisms (under different types of selection);

(b) there is no particular pattern to the substitutions indicating that selection is not eliminating some variations;

(c) the rate of mutation is relatively high and has remained relatively constant for millions of years even though environments have fluctuated greatly over that period of time;

(d) certain regions of molecules and certain functions of those molecules should logically be less likely to have amino acid substitutions influence the phenotype.

e) the rate of amino acid substitution in some proteins is much too high to have been produced by selection. The *selectionists* suggest that even though amino acid substitutions *appear* to be neutral, it is more likely that their influence has just not been determined. In addition, they point out that many polymorphisms are clearly maintained in the population *by* selection.

11. Like many other debates which surround the nature of evolution, it is important to see that debate is a natural component of scientific understanding. It is likely that some genes (like histones) will not tolerate nucleotide substitutions to a significant degree and the neutral mutation theory will not hold.

However, there are other genes which produce quite variable products and provide support for the neutral mutation theory. Usually controversy is resolved as one dives deeper into the problem and seeks to define the variables and complexities of the process. It is controversy which stimulates a desire to seek answers. The genetic concept of evolution is based on the assumption that genetic change influences levels of fitness. This assumption is favored over "non-gene" alternatives. Examining nucleic acid changes in non-coding regions does give a great deal of information about evolutionary processes. While not being a strong force in evolution, as far as we know, it does not negate our view of genetic change as a force in evolution.

Chapter 24: Conservative Genetics

Concept Areas	Corresponding Problems
Population Dynamics	1, 3
Genetic Assessment of Threatened Species	1
Management of Threatened Species	2, 5, 6, 7
Inbreeding and Drift in Small Populations	3, 4, 6

Structures and Substances

Pacific yew (*Taxus brevifolia*)

Grey wolf (*Canis lupus*)

California condors

   (*Gymnogyps californianus*)

Russian wheat aphid (*Diuraphis noxia*)

Antarctic fur seal (*Arctocephalus sp.*)

Cheetah (*Acinonyx jubatus*)

North American brown bear

   (*Ursus arctos*)

Peppered moth (*Biston betularia*)

Fruit fly (*Drosophila melanogaster*)

Black-footed ferret (*Mustela nigripes*)

Native rock grape (*Vitis rupestris*)

Domesticated species

Isozyme

DNA profile

   nuclear

   mitochondrial

   chloroplast

Harmonic mean

Core collection

Processes/Methods

Human population growth

Biodiversity

   human impact

Conservation genetics

Intraspecific diversity

   interpopulation

   intrapopulation

Interspecific diversity

Loss of genetic diversity

    reduced population size

    habitat loss

    population fragmentation

Detection of genetic diversity

    isozyme analysis

    RFLP

    PCR

    AFLP (amplified fragment length polymorphism)

Absolute population size (N)

    effective populaton size (N_e)

    $N_e = 4(N_m N_f)/(N_m + N_f)$

    $N_e = 1/(1/t)(1/N_1 + 1/N_2 + 1/N_3 \ldots)$

Population bottlenexk

Founder effect

Genetic drift

Concepts

Vulnerable and endangered species

Genetic diversity

Loss of genetic diversity

    population size

Population dynamics

    bottleneck

    founder effect

    genetic drift

    inbreeding

    gene flow

    genetic erosion

Conservation strategies

Probability of fixation p(A)

Inbreeding coefficient

    $F = (2pq - H)/2pq$

    $H_t = (1-1/2N_e)^t H_o$

    inbreeding depression]

Genetic load

    purging genetic load

Gene flow relates to migration

Genetic erosion (loss of diversity)

Ex situ and *In situ* conservation

    captive species

    gene banks

Population augmentation

    outbreeding depression

Solutions to Problems
and Discussion Questions

1. (a) Apply the formula which computes the effective population size as the harmonic mean of the numbers in each generation:

$$N_e = 1/(1/t)(1/N_1 + 1/N_2 + 1/N_3 \ldots)$$

Substituting the values:

$$N_e = 1/(1/4)(1/47 + 1/17 + 1/20 + 1/35)$$

$$N_e = 25.21$$

(b) Apply the formula which computes the frequency of heterozygotes after t generations as a function of effective population size:

$$H_t = (1-1/2N_e)^t H_o$$

Substituting the values:

$$H_t = (1-1/2(25.21))^4(.55)$$

$$H_t = .5073$$

(c) Apply the foumula which relates the inbreeding coefficient to the frequency of heterozygotes in a population:

$$F = (2pq - H)/2pq$$

$$F = (.55 - .5073)/.55$$

$$F = 0.0776$$

2. The frequency of the lethal gene in the captive population ($q^2 = 5/169$ and $q = .172$) is approximately double that in the gene pool as a whole ($q = 0.09$). Applying the formula

$$q_n = q_o/(1 + nq_o)$$

one can estimate that it would take 10 generations to reduce the lethal gene's frequency to .063 in the captive population with no intervention (random mating assumed). Since condors produce very few eggs per year, a more proactive approach seems justified. First, if detailed records are kept of the breeding partners of the captive birds, then knowledge of heterozygotes should be available.

Breeding programs could be established to restrict matings between those carrying the lethal gene. Such "kinship management" is often used in captive populations. If kinship records are not available, it is often possible to establish kinship using genetic markers such as DNA microsatellite polymorphisms. Using such markers, one can often identify mating partners and link them to their offspring.

By coupling knowledge of mating partners with the likelihood of producing a lethal genetic combination, selective matings can often be used to minimize the influence of a deleterious gene. In addition, such markers can be used to establish matings which optimize genetic mixing, thus reducing inbreeding depression.

3. Notice (in the *Essentials* text) that the probability of fixation through drift is the same as a gene's initial freqency. In this problem, the probability of A being fixed (and therefore a lost) is 0.75. The probability of B being fixed (and b being lost) is 0.8 and the probability of C being fixed (and c being lost) is 0.95. Therefore the probability that all the recessive alleles will be lost through genetic drift is

$$0.75 \times 0.80 \times 0.95 = 0.57$$

4. Both genetic drift and inbreeding tend to drive populations toward homozygosity. Genetic drift is more common when the effective breeding size of the population is low. When this condition prevails, inbreeding is also much more likely. They are different in that inbreeding can occur when certain population structures or behaviors favor matings between relatives, regardless of the effective size of the population. Inbreeding tends to increase the frequency of both homozygous classes at the expense of the heterozygotes. Genetic drift can lead to fixation of one allele or the other, thus producing a single homozygous class.

5. There are a number of dangers inherent in the management of such a small herd of endangered rhinos. Because of the small breeding pool, inbreeding depression is likely to lead to less fit individuals over time. To combat this problem, genetic markers (such as microsatellites) can be used to assess the general degree of relatedness and heterozygosity of each of the 16 rhinos. From such information, appropriate matings can be facilitated with would reduce inbreeding depression. However, additional efforts may be needed in this extreme case. It is possible to develop exchange programs whereby animals from other herds provide semen (either naturally or artificially) thereby reducing inbreeding. This practice can be successful if females are receptive and if no deleterious genes are brought into the population (outbreeding depression).

Population augmentation, where individuals are transplanted into a declining population, can be used to increase numbers and genetic diversity. However, as stated above, outbreeding depression accompanies this practice

Sometimes drastic measures must be taken in extreme cases such as the black rhino. Dehorning is often practiced to remove the incentive for poaching and reduce lethal wounding due to fighting. This practice is only useful in areas void of dangerous predators.

6. Inbreeding depression, over time, reduces the level of heterozygosity, usually a selectively advantageous quality of a species. When homozygosity increases (through loss of heterozygosity) deleterious alleles are likely to become more of a load on a population. Outbreeding depression occurs when there is a reduction in fitness of progeny from genetically diverse individuals. It is usually attributed to offspring being less well-adapted to the local environmental conditions of the parents.

Even though forced outbreeding may be necessary to save a threatened species, where population numbers are low, it significantly and permanently changes the genetic make-up of the the species.

7. Cloning of some highly threatened species may be the only way to save that species from extinction. However, the long-term disadvantages of cloning for this purpose are often considered self-defeating. With cloning one "short-circuits" normal processes (meiosis, gametic union, *etc.*) necessary to maintain genetic variation. With a loss of genetic variation comes difficulties with adaptation as environments change. It may be possible to identify certain conditions in which cloning would be useful to "save" a species, however, interbreeding provides benefits which allow a species to evolve. In addition, as members of a species become more uniform (through clonng) they are more likely to suffer more severe and widespread responses to disease and environmental stress.

Sample Test Questions
(detailed explanations of answers follow in next section)

How to use this section:

The purpose of these *Sample Test Questions* is to present a slightly different style of question.

1. Set aside several hours of study time, perhaps a week before each examination.

2. Select two questions from each chapter covered on your upcoming test. Attempt to work selected questions, five or so per hour, under test conditions. Do not use the text as an aid at this point. You need to struggle on your own. **Write down your answers on paper**, then, *after* you have finished the "test," check your answers.

3. If you are having difficulty, then you are weak one or more of the concept areas listed for each question. Review the corresponding material in the text, then include the missed question in a subsequent practice test.

4. Under each question indicate your level of mastery.

If you have made mistakes, take comfort, there are many places to make mistakes on these problems. Some of the students who made the same mistakes are now practicing geneticists!

Ch.1 Ques.1 In 1859, Charles Darwin published *The Origin of Species* in which he presented ideas on the causes of organismic change through time. A primary conceptual gap existed which left his theory open to criticism. What was that conceptual gap?

Mastery: complete____, partial____, nil____

Ch.1 Ques.2 Name the individual who, working with the garden pea in the mid-1850s, demonstrated quantitative patterns of heredity and developed a theory involving the behavior of hereditary factors.

Mastery: complete____, partial____, nil____

Ch.1 Ques.3 What does the term "genetics" mean?

Mastery: complete____, partial____, nil____

Ch.1 Ques.4 Name the substance which serves as the hereditary material in eukaryotes and prokaryotes.

Mastery: complete____, partial____, nil____

Ch.1, 2 Ques.5 When examining chromosomes from a single nucleus of an individual cell, it is often possible to match up chromosomes on the basis of overall size, centromere position, and sometimes other physical characteristics. Chromosomes which can be matched up or paired are called _____.

Mastery: complete____, partial____, nil____

Ch.1, 2 Ques.6 Regarding chromosomal constituents, what is a fundamental difference between processes of mitosis and meiosis?

Mastery: complete____, partial____, nil____

Ch.1 Ques.7 List three components of the genetic material, DNA.

Mastery: complete____, partial____, nil____

> **For the above questions from Chapters 1 and 2, there are few major concepts. Chapter 1 serves as an introduction. Test Questions are primarily oriented toward reading retention and study effort.**

Ch.2 Ques.8 The mosquito, *Culex pipiens*, has a diploid chromosome number of 6. Assume that one chromosome pair is metacentric, and the other two pairs are acrocentric.

(a) Draw chromosomal configurations which one would expect to see at the following stages: primary oocyte (metaphase I), secondary spermatocyte (metaphase II).

(b) Assuming that a G_1 nucleus in *Culex* contains about 20 picograms (pg) of DNA, how much DNA would you expect in the following nuclei; Primary Spermatocyte, First Polar Body, Secondary Oocyte, Ootid in G_1 phase?

(c) Assume that a female mosquito is heterozygous for the recessive gene *wavy bristles* (symbolized as *wb*) and this gene locus is on an acrocentric chromosome. Draw an expected mitotic metaphase with the appropriate genetic labeling pattern.

> **Concepts:**
> **chromosome mechanics**
> **mitosis, meiosis**
> **symbolism**
> **DNA content (cell cycles)**

Mastery: complete____, partial____, nil____

Ch.2 Ques.9 In humans, chromosome #1 is large and metacentric, the X chromosome is medium in size and submetacentric (submedian), while the Y chromosome is small and acrocentric. Assume that you were microscopically examining human chromosomes at the stages given below.

(a) Illustrate (draw) the above-mentioned (#1, X and/or Y) chromosomes and/or pairs at the stages given (several different configurations may be applicable in some cases):

Metaphase I (Primary Oocyte):
First Polar Body:
Secondary Spermatocyte:
Secondary Oocyte:

(b) The Rh blood group locus is on Chromosome #1. Individuals are *DD* or *Dd* if Rh+ and *dd* if
Rh-. The locus for glucose-6-phosphate-dehydrogenase deficiency (G6PD) is located on the X chromosome. There are two alternatives at this locus, + and -. For each of the above cells, place genes (using symbolism given) on chromosomes if the female is heterozygous at both the Rh and G6PD loci. Do the same for the secondary spermatocyte (above) assuming that the male is Rh-, and + for the G6PD locus.

(c) Assume that the average DNA content per G_1 nucleus in humans is 6.5 picograms. For the nuclei (including the entire chromosome complement for each nucleus) presented, give the expected DNA content:

Metaphase I (Primary Oocyte):
First Polar Body:
Secondary Spermatocyte:
Secondary Oocyte:

> **Concepts:**
> **chromosome mechanics**
> **mitosis, meiosis**
> **symbolism**
> **DNA content (cell cycles)**

Mastery: complete____, partial____, nil____

Ch.2 Ques.10 Assume that you are examining a cell under a microscope and you observe the following as the total chromosomal constituents of a nucleus. You know that 2n = 2 in this organism, that all chromosomes are telocentric, and that each G$_1$ cell nucleus contains 8 picograms of DNA.

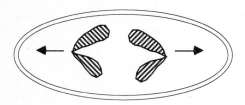

(a) Circle the correct stage for this cell:

anaphase of mitosis

anaphase of meiosis I

anaphase of meiosis II

telophase of mitosis

(b) How many picograms of chromosomal DNA would you expect in the cell shown above?

> **Concepts:**
> **chromosome morphology**
> **telocentric, etc.**
> **anaphase configurations**
> **chromosome mechanics**
> **meiosis, mitosis**
> **DNA content in cell cycles**

Mastery: complete____, partial____, nil____

Chs.2,4 Ques.11 The genes for *singed bristles* (*sn*) and *miniature wings* (*m*) are recessive and located on the X chromosome in *Drosophila melanogaster*. In a cross between a singed-bristled, miniature-winged female and a wild type male, all of the male offspring were singed-miniature.

(a) Draw meiotic metaphase I chromosomal configurations which represent the X and/or Y chromosomes of the parental (singed-miniature female and wild type male) flies. Place gene symbols (*sn*, *m*) and their wild type alleles (*sn*$^+$, *m*$^+$) on appropriate chromosomes.

(b) Draw a mitotic metaphase chromosomal configuration that represents the X and/or Y chromosomes of the F1 male. Place gene symbols (*sn*, *m*) on appropriate chromosomes.

(c) Most of the female offspring from the above-mentioned cross were phenotypically wild type; however, one exceptional female was recovered which had singed bristles and miniature wings. Given that meiotic nondisjunction accounted for this exceptional female, would you expect it to have occurred in the parental male of parental female?

(d) Draw a meiotic, labeled (with gene symbols) circumstance and division product(s) which could account for the exceptional female described above. (Confine your drawing to X chromosomes only).

> **Concepts:**
> **chromosome mechanics**
> **meiosis**
> **symbolism**
> **meiotic nondisjunction**
> **sex-linkage**

Mastery: complete____, partial____, nil____

Ch.2 Ques.12 The red fox (*Vulpes vulpes*) has 17 pairs of somewhat long chromosomes. The Arctic fox (*Alopex lagopus*) has 26 pairs of somewhat shorter chromosomes.

(a) If a female red fox is crossed with a male Arctic fox, what will be the chromosome number in the somatic tissues of the hybrid?

(b) Assume that a somatic G_1 nucleus of the Arctic fox contains 12 picograms of DNA while a somatic G_1 nucleus of the red fox contains 8 picograms of DNA. How much nuclear DNA could you expect in a G_2 somatic nucleus of the hybrid?

Concepts:
   meiosis and chromosome numbers
   DNA content

Mastery: complete____, partial____, nil____

Chs.3,4 Ques.13 Red-green colorblindness is inherited in man as an X-linked, recessive gene. Using the symbols below, draw a pedigree which is consistent with the following statements.

A phenotypically normal woman is married to a phenotypically normal man. The woman's parents are phenotypically normal but her maternal grandfather is colorblind. The woman's paternal grandparents as well as her maternal grandmother are phenotypically normal.

male	= □
female	= ○
Rg	= normal color sight
rg	= colorblind

What is the probability that the first son born to the woman will be phenotypically normal (not be colorblind)?

Concepts:
   sex-linked inheritance (X-linked)
   pedigree construction
   probability (product rule)

Mastery: complete____, partial____, nil____

Chs.3,4 Ques.14 In a *Drosophila*, experiment a cross is made between a homozygous wild type female and a tan-bodied (mutant) male. All the resulting F_1 flies were phenotypically wild type. Adult flies of the F_2 generation (from a mating of the F_1's) had the following characteristics:

Sex	*Phenotype*	*Number*
Male	wild	346
Male	tan	329
Female	wild	702

(a) Using conventional symbolism, illustrate the genotype, *on an appropriate chromosomal configuration*, of a secondary oocyte nucleus of one of the F_1 females. Be certain to distinguish the X chromosomes from the autosomes. Note: *Drosophila melanogaster* has a diploid chromosome number of 8.

(b) Using the same conventional symbolism, give the genotype *on an appropriate chromosomal configuration* of a primary spermatocyte of the tan-bodied F_2 males.

Concepts:
   sex-linked inheritance (X-linked)
   chromosome mechanics
      meiosis
   conventional symbolism

Mastery: complete____, partial____, nil____

Ch.3 Ques.15 *Gray* seed color in peas is dominant to *white*. Assume that Mendel conducted a series of experiments where plants were crossed and offspring classified according to the table below. What are the most probable genotypes of each parent?

Parents			Progeny	
			gray	white
(a) gray	X	white	81	79
(b) gray	X	gray	120	42
(c) white	X	white	0	50
(d) gray	X	white	74	0

Concepts:
   Mendelian genetics
      monohybrid cross
   dominance/recessiveness
   3:1 and 1:1 ratios

Mastery: complete____, partial____, nil____

Chs.3,4 Ques.16 Hemophilia (type A) is recessive and X-linked in humans, whereas the ABO blood groups locus is autosomal. Assume that the following matings were examined for the transmission of these genes. Give the expected phenotypes and numbers assuming 800 offspring are produced.

Group A: Females heterozygous for hemophilia with blood type AB mated to normal males with blood group O.

Group B: Females heterozygous for hemophilia with blood type AB mated to males with hemophilia and blood group AB.

Concepts:
   sex-linkage (X-linked)
   autosomal inheritance
   dihybrid situation
   incomplete dominance
   complete dominance

Mastery: complete____, partial____, nil____

Ch.3 Ques.17 For the cross *PpRr* X *pprr* where complete dominance and independent assortment hold, assume that you received the following results and you wished to determine whether they differ significantly (in a statistical sense) from expectation.

PR phenotypes	=	40
Pr phenotypes	=	10
pR phenotypes	=	20
pr phenotypes	=	30

(a) State the null hypothesis associated with this test of significance.

(b) How many degrees of freedom would be associated with this test of significance?

(c) Assuming that a Chi-Square value of 20.00 is arrived at in this test of significance, do you accept or reject the null hypothesis?

Degrees of Freedom	P = 0.05
1	3.84
2	5.99
3	7.82
4	9.49
5	11.07

Concepts:
   Mendelian patterns
      1:1:1:1 ratio
   null hypothesis
   expected values
   χ^2 analysis
   interpretation of χ^2

Mastery: complete____, partial____, nil____

Chs.2,4,5 Ques. 18 Explain the processes, genotypic, chromosomal, and developmental, which would lead to a bilateral gynandromorph in *Drosophila melanogaster* in which, starting from a fully heterozygous zygote, the eventual male half of the fly has white eyes and singed bristles, while the female half is phenotypically wild type.

> **Concepts:**
> **sex-linked inheritance (X-linked)**
> **gynandromorph production**
> **sex determination in *Drosophila***
> **insect development**
> **mitosis, nondisjunction**

Mastery: complete___, partial___, nil___

Chs.2,3,6 Ques.19 Describe and exemplify similarities and differences between *discontinuous* and *continuous* traits at the *molecular* and *transmission* levels.

> **Concepts:**
> **interaction of gene products**
> **relationship between genotype**
> **and phenotype**
> **multi-factor inheritance**

Mastery: complete___, partial___, nil___

Chs.2,8 Ques.20 Assume that there are 18 map units between two loci in the mouse and that you are able to microscopically observe meiotic chromosomes in this organism. If you examined 150 primary oocytes, in how many would you expect to see a chiasma between the two loci mentioned above?

> **Concepts:**
> **crossing over mechanisms**
> **meiosis**
> **gene mapping**
> **chromosome mechanics**

Mastery: complete___, partial___, nil___

Ch.8 Ques.21 Given below are two dihybrid crosses between various strains of *Drosophila*. To the right of each are map distances known to exist between the genes involved. For each cross give the phenotypes of the offspring and the percentages expected for each.

	Mating		
	Female	*Male*	*Map distance*
(a)	AB/ab	ab/ab	20
(b)	ab/ab	AB/ab	20

> **Concepts:**
> **linkage and crossing over**
> **computation of map units**
> **complete linkage**
> **independent assortment**
> **lack of crossing over in males**

Mastery: complete___, partial___, nil___

Ch.8 Ques.22 Given below are two dihybrid crosses between various strains of *Drosophila*. To the right of each are map distances known to exist between the genes involved. For each cross give the phenotypes of the offspring and the percentages expected for each.

	Mating		
	Female	*Male*	*Map distance*
(a)	Pq/pQ	pq/pq	50
(b)	DB/db	db/db	0

> **Concepts:**
> **linkage and crossing over**
> **computation of map units**
> **complete linkage**
> **independent assortment**
> **lack of crossing over in males**

Mastery: complete___, partial___, nil___

Chs.9, 10, 11, 14 Ques.23 The foundations of molecular genetics rest upon the assumption that a genetic material exists with the following properties:

a. Autocatalytic (can replicate itself)

b. Heterocatalytic (can direct form and function)

c. Mutable

d. Can exist in an infinite number of forms

(a) Provide a simple sketch which demonstrates the replication scheme of DNA.

(b) Briefly describe how DNA provides form and function.

(c) At the level of nucleotides, what character-izes mutant DNA?

(d) Why may we say that DNA can exist in an infinite number of forms?

```
Concepts:
    understanding of gene function
    understanding DNA structure
    function
    mutation
    variation
```

Mastery: complete____, partial____, nil____

Ch. 10 Ques.24 On the graph below, draw $C_o t$ curves for DNA from two genomes, one lacking repetitive DNA and the other containing repetitive DNA. Indicate the point on each curve at which the renaturation is half-complete. Label the horizontal and vertical axes accordingly. Explain the molecular basis for the different curves.

```
Concepts:
    nucleic acid hybridization
    hybridization kinetics
    $C_o t$ curves
```

Mastery: complete____, partial____, nil____

Chs. 10, 11 Ques.25 Given below is a single-stranded nucleotide sequence. Answer questions which refer to this sequence.

a. In the circle at the bottom of this sequence, place a 5' or 3', whichever corresponds.

b. Is the above structure an RNA or DNA? State which_____.

c. Assume that a complementary strand is produced in which all the innermost phosphates of the adenine triphosphonucleotide precursors are labeled with ^{32}P. What bases would be labeled if the complementary strand is completely degraded with spleen diesterase (cleaves between the phosphate and the 5'carbon)?_____.

d, What bases would be labeled if the complementary strand was completely degraded with snake venom diesterase (cleaves between the phosphate and the 3' carbon)?_____.

Concepts:
>   **DNA and RNA structure**
>   **complementarity**
>   **5', 3' orientations**
>   **degradation products**

Mastery: complete____, partial____, nil____

Ch.11 Ques.26 Assume that you were able to culture a strain of *E. coli* in medium containing either "normal" nitrogen or a heavy isotope of nitrogen (^{15}N). You grow the bacteria for a time in ^{15}N-containing medium which permits one complete replication of the bacterial chromosome. You extract the DNA, calling this extraction A. You continue to grow the bacterial culture in the ^{15}N DNA for a time, which permits one more complete round of chromosome replication. You again extract the DNA, calling this extraction B. Assuming that non-labeled DNA has a density of 1.6 and that fully labeled DNA (that is with **all** the ^{14}N replaced with ^{15}N) has a density of 1.9, construct sedimentation profiles which reflect the expected densities of DNA from extractions A and B.

Extraction A

Extraction B

Heat-treated B

1.6	1.9

Density

Knowing that heating DNA to 100° C. causes separation of complementary strands, use a broken line (- - -) to indicate the sedimentation profile of heat denaturation of extraction B DNA.

Concepts:
>   **semiconservative replication**
>   **labeling**
>   **centrifugation**
>   **denaturation**

Mastery: complete____, partial____, nil____

Chs.10,11 Ques.27 Assume that you are microscopically examining mitotic metaphase cells of an organism with a 2N chromosome number of 2 (both telocentric). Assume also that the cell passed through one S phase labeling (innermost phosphate of dCTP radioactive) just prior to the period of observation.

(a) Draw this cell's chromosomes, and the autoradiographic pattern you would expect to see.

(b) Assuming that the A+T/G+C ratio of the DNA in this cell is 1.67 and this DNA is digested with snake venom diesterase (cleaves at the 3' position), what percentages of the total radioactivity would the following products have?

Adenine_____   Guanine_____

Thymine_____   Cytosine_____

Concepts:
>   **semiconservative replication**
>   **chromosome morphology**
>   **DNA structure**
>   **labeling**
>   **enzymatic digestion**
>   **5', 3' orientations**

Mastery: complete____, partial____, nil____

Ch. 11 Ques. 28 Drawn below is a diagram (not to scale) of DNA in the process of replication. Numbered arrows point to specific structures which you are to identify in the corresponding spaces below:

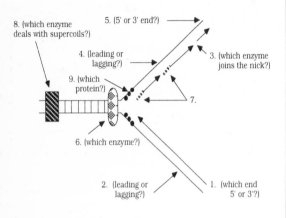

8. (which enzyme deals with supercoils?)

5. (5' or 3' end?)

4. (leading or lagging?)

3. (which enzyme joins the nick?)

9. (which protein?)

7.

6. (which enzyme?)

2. (leading or lagging?)

1. (which end 5' or 3'?)

1.   2.   3.

4.   5.   6.

7.   8.   9.

Concepts:
   overall DNA replication
   5', 3' polarity restrictions
   enzymology
   priming

Mastery: complete____, partial____, nil____

Ch. 12 Ques. 29 Below is a schematic of transcription and translation occurring simultaneously as described by Miller *et al.* (1970) in *E. coli*. The broken circle represents the enzyme RNA polymerase. Answer the questions below.

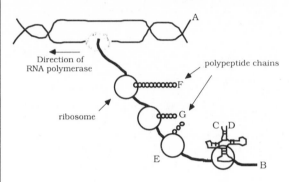

Direction of RNA polymerase

polypeptide chains

ribosome

A

F

G

C D

E

B

1. Is "A" at the 5' or 3' end of the DNA strand?
   _____

2. Is "B" at the 5' or 3' end of the RNA strand?
   _____

3. Is "C" at the 5' or 3' end of the RNA strand?
   _____

4. What type of RNA is closest to letter "D"?
   _____

5. Would base sequences near letters "C" or "D" (state which) be expected to hold the amino acid?   _____

6. What is the S value of the rRNA in the small subunit of the ribosome closest to letter "E"?   _____

7. Is the amino acid nearest letter "F" the same type as the one nearest letter "G" (yes or no)?   _____

Concepts:
   transcription
      5', 3' orientations
   translation
      tRNA orientation
      rRNA in ribosomes

Mastery: complete____, partial____, nil____

Chs.13,14 Ques.30 Assume that the following sequence of amino acids occurs in a protein starting from the "N" terminus (with asp) of a large polypeptide chain:

asp-glu-ile-leu-ser-thr-met-arg-tyr-try-phe-gly

Assume that gene *X* is responsible for synthesis of this gene. Answer the questions below.

(a) Which amino acid(s) would you expect to change if gene *X* is altered by the mutagen, 2-amino purine, such that a transition mutation occurred which caused a change in the 9th base of the mRNA (counting from the 5' end of the coding region)?

(b) Which amino acid(s) would you expect to change if gene *X* is altered by mutagen, such as acridine orange, such that a frameshift mutation occurred which caused an insertion of a base between bases 3 and 4 of the mRNA (counting from the 5' end of the coding region)?

(c) Which amino acid(s) would you expect to change if gene *X* is altered by the mutagen, nitrous acid, such that a mutation occurred which caused a change in the 11th base of the mRNA (counting from the 5' end of the coding region)?

> **Concepts:**
>   **translation**
>   **coding**
>   **mutation**

Mastery: complete____, partial____, nil____

Chs.13, 14 Ques.31 Below is a set of experimental results relating the growth (+) of *Neurospora* on several media. Based on the information provided, present the biochemical pathway and the locations of the metabolic blocks.

Strain	Medium		
	MM	MM+A	MM+B
t409	-	+	+
t410	+	+	+
r3	-	-	+

> **Concepts:**
>   **pathway analysis**
>   **Beadle and Tatum "set-up"**
>   **biochemical (nutritional) phenotype**

Mastery: complete____, partial____, nil____

Ch. 13 Ques.32 Drawn below is a hypothetical protein which contains areas where various types of bonds might be expected to occur. For each area a circle is drawn and in that circle is placed a number. In the corresponding spaces below, state which bond type (or interaction) is most likely illustrated **and** state how that particular type of bond (or interaction) is formed. *You may use a given bond type only once.*

1.

2.

3.

4. What type of amino acids tend to be located on the outside (water side) of the molecule?

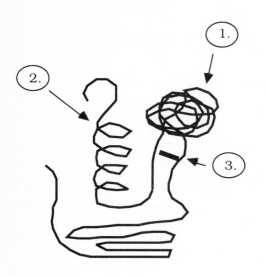

```
Concepts:
    importance of primary structure
    varieties of bonds
    "higher level" folding
    structure/function relationships
```

Mastery: complete____, partial____, nil____

Ch.15 Ques.33 Depending on the regulatory system, in prokaryotes when the regulatory protein **is** or **isn't** bound to the DNA, the operon may be **on** or **off**. Fill in the chart below and give a brief explanation of your reasoning.

Relationship of Regulator Protein to DNA	Operator	
	Positive control	*Negative control*
is bound		
isn't bound		

Concepts:
genetic regulation
positive vs. negative control

Mastery: complete____, partial____, nil____

Ch.15 Ques.34 Some eukaryotes have evolved mechanisms for obtaining more than one kind of protein from a single transcription unit (a transcription unit simply being a stretch of DNA that is transcribed into a single primary RNA transcript). Describe such a mechanism.

Concepts:
differential or alternative
RNA splicing

Mastery: complete____, partial____, nil____

Chs.15,16 Ques.35 DNase is often used to map the locations where DNA-binding proteins (histones, RNA polymerases, transcription factors, etc.) interact with DNA. Restriction endonucleases are used to cut DNA for identification and cloning. Why are these two different enzyme classes used in these different ways?

Concepts:
experimental strategies
action of nucleases
DNase
restriction endonucleases

Mastery: complete____, partial____, nil____

Ch.16 Ques.36 Assume that you have a cDNA clone for the gene causing retinoblastoma, and you prepare Southern blots probing DNA in cells from normal individuals and from children with retinoblastoma. Genomic DNA is prepared using the restriction endonuclease *Hind*III (the *Rb* gene contains four *Hind*III fragments as indicated below), and the following hybridization appears:

Southern blot

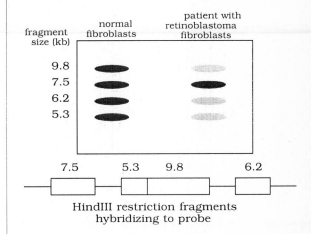

HindIII restriction fragments hybridizing to probe

What does each band represent?

What conclusions can be drawn from these data?

Concepts:
experimental strategies
    cDNA probes
    Southern blots
    electrophoresis
    restriction endonuclease analysis
    hybridization

Mastery: complete____, partial____, nil____

Ch. 16 Ques. 37 The *thioredoxin* gene in bacteria aids in the necessary reduction of proteins. It encodes a protein of 108 amino acids and is contained in a 0.9 kb (*PstI/BamHI*) fragment. The gene for kanamycin resistance is contained in a 1.4 kb (*BamHI/PstI*) fragment. The restriction map (one orientation) of these two genes (flanked by *BamHI* sites) in a plasmid vector is presented below.

(A)

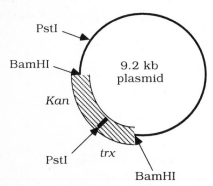

(a) Assume that the plasmid is restricted with the enzyme *BamHI*. What would be the electrophoretic pattern of the cleaved fragments?

(b) Assume that the orientation given above is only a guess and that the *Bam* HI fragment containing the *trx* and *Kan* genes could possibly exist in the opposite orientation (B). What experiment would you perform to determine whether the orientation is as in (A) or (B)?

(B)

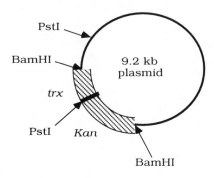

Concepts:
experimental strategies
electrophoresis
restriction digestion
        fragment analysis

Mastery: complete____, partial____, nil____

Ch.16 Ques.38 The Maxam and Gilbert DNA sequencing procedure involves chemical reactions (methylation) and cleavages (piperidine) that produce ^{32}P-labeled DNA fragments. The chemical reagents can give rise to G, G+A, C, and C+T cleavages. These fragments are then separated on electrophoretic gels, and the sequence is read directly from the gel. A sample gel is given below. From this gel, provide the sequence of the DNA fragment.

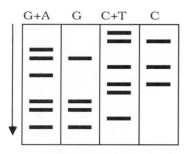

G+A   G   C+T   C

Small fragments
at this end of gel

> Concepts:
>   electrophoresis
>   DNA sequencing

Mastery: complete____, partial____, nil____

Ch.16 Ques.39 A prevalent method of DNA sequencing is based on the use of a dideoxynucleotide (ddNTP) to bring about deliberate chain termation. Specifically, how does a dideoxynucleotide cause chain termination and how is it used to determine a base sequence? Give the sequence depicted in the gel below:

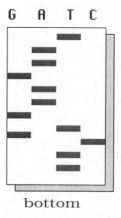

G A T C

bottom

> Concepts:
>   DNA polymerization
>   3'OH dependence
>   gel electrophoresis

Mastery: complete____, partial____, nil____

Ch. 17 Ques. 40 Provide an overview of similarities and differences among viral, prokaryotic and eukaryotic chromosomes. What are histones and how are they involved in chromosome structure?

> Concepts:
>   chromosome morphology
>   chromosome folding

Mastery: complete____, partial____, nil____

Ch. 17 Ques. 41 Describe "specialized chromosomes" in eukaryotes. What is a chromosome "puff" and what is its significance?

> **Concepts:**
> **special chromosomes**
> **gene activity and autoradiography**

Mastery: complete____, partial____, nil____

Ch. 18 Ques. 42 (a) Describe the general structure of an antibody molecule and the manner in which antibody variability is established.

(b) Assuming that a light chain has 300 V and 10 J regions and the heavy chain has 300 V, 10 D, and 10 J regions, about how many different immunoglobin light-chain genes and how many different heavy-chain genes could theoretically be formed in this organism? Assume that all joining is precise and no nucleotides are lost or gained during recombination within the chains.

(c) How many different immunoglobin molecules could be generated from these heavy and light chains?

> **Concepts:**
> **immunoglobin structure**
> **gene recombination**
> **association of chains**

Mastery: complete____, partial____, nil____

Ch. 18 Ques 43 What is meant by the term proteomics? Speculate on the role of proteomics in interpreting data from the Human Genome Project.

> **Concepts:**
> **gene function in time and space**
> **genotype/phenotype relationships**

Mastery: complete____, partial____, nil____

Ch. 19 Ques 44 (List and briefly describe three major classes of Gene Therapy. What are major ethical issues related to Gene Therapy?

> **Concepts:**
> **general classification**
> **common ethical concerns**

Mastery: complete____, partial____, nil____

Ch. 19 Ques. 45 The study of human genetics is complicated by the fact that many traits of interest are determined by more than one gene pair and are often characterized by variation in penetrance and expressivity. The study of human genetics suffers additional complications.

(a) List three of these additional complications.

(b) The neurological disorder of Huntington's disease is caused by an autosomal dominant gene, yet in pedigrees it may show incomplete penetrance. Why?

(c) Twin studies have greatly facilitated our understanding of such human traits as schizophrenia and manic-depression. Why?

(d) What factors are believed to influence the expressivity of human traits?

Concepts:
  **experimental approaches to
    human genetics
  twin studies
  penetrance, expressivity**

Mastery: complete____, partial____, nil____

Ch.20 Ques.46 Two terms, *determination* and *differentiation,* are consistently used in discussions of development.

(a) Provide a brief definition of each term.

(b) Which, *determination* or *differentiation,* comes first during development of *Drosophila*, for example?

Concepts:
  **terms
    determination
    differentiation
  relationships
  Drosophila development**

Mastery: complete____, partial____, nil____

Ch.20 Ques.47 Development may be defined as the attainment of a differentiated state. Given that all cells of a eukaryote probably contain the same complete set of genes, how do we currently explain development in terms of gene activity? What evidence supports your explanation?

Concepts:
  **variable gene activity hypothesis
  genomic equivalence
  evidence for differential
    transcription**

Mastery: complete____, partial____, nil____

Ch.22 Ques.48 Assume that in a particular population, approximately 8% of the males show red-green colorblindness. Knowing that this form of colorblindness is X-linked, what percentage of the females would be expected to be colorblind?

What would be the expected frequency of heterozygous females?

Assuming that the Hardy-Weinberg equilibrium assumptions pertain, what percentage of men will be colorblind in the next generation?

Concepts:
  **Hardy-Weinberg applications to
    X-linked gene
  maintenance of gene frequencies
    over time**

Mastery: complete____, partial____, nil____

Ch.22, 23 Ques.49 List and briefly describe factors which change gene frequencies in populations. Is inbreeding a factor in changing gene frequencies? Explain.

Concepts:
  **factors which change gene
    frequencies
  influence of inbreeding on gene
    frequencies**

Mastery: complete____, partial____, nil____

191

Ch.23 Ques.50 A *species* is often defined as a population of interbreeding or potentially inter-breeding organisms reproductively isolated from other such populations. Given such an isolated population, will speciation (formation of a new species) occur if the Hardy-Weinberg assumptions are met?

> **Concept:**
> **relationship between speciation**
> **and Hardy-Weinberg assumptions**

Mastery: complete____, partial____, nil____

Ch.24 Ques.51 Compare and contrast the phenomena of inbreeding and outbreeding depression. What impact would each have on the long-term survival of a natural population?

> **Concept:**
> **natural and artificial breeding**
> **patterns**
> **genetic homozygosity and survival**

Mastery: complete____, partial____, nil____

The Next Section Contains Answers

Ch.1 Ques.1 lack of understanding of the genetic basis of variation and inheritance

Ch.1 Ques.2 Gregor Mendel

Ch.1 Ques.3 Genetics is a subdiscipline of biology concerned with the study of heredity and variation at the molecular, cellular, developmental, organismal, and populational levels.

Ch.1 Ques.4 DNA or deoxyribonucleic acid is the hereditary material in eukaryotes and prokaryotes. Either DNA or RNA (ribonucleic acid) serves in viruses.

Ch.1, 2 Ques.5 homologous

Ch.1, 2 Ques.6 In mitosis, chromosome number remains constant, while in meiosis, chromosome number is reduced by half in the final products. In meiosis, there is pairing of homologous chromosomes.

Ch.1 Ques.7 nitrogenous bases, phosphate, deoxyribose sugar

Ch.2 Ques.8 This question is intended to determine your understanding of mitosis, chromosome morphology, symbolism, the positioning of genes on chromosomes, and the changes in DNA content through the cell cycles. **(a)** Since the diploid chromosome number is six, there will be three bivalents, one involving metacentrics, and two involving acrocentrics in a primary oocyte. We can draw the chromosomes of the primary oocyte as follows:

Note: homologous chromosomes will have "slashes" going in opposite directions because of the shadowing used to depict maternal and paternal chromosomes.

Since secondary spermatocytes arise after meiosis I, there should be only dyads, one metacentric and two acrocentric, and they should be aligned end-to-end as indicated in the above drawing .

(b) Given that there are about 20 picograms of DNA in a G_1 nucleus, we would expect there to be 40pg in a G_2 nucleus (after S phase) and 40pg to the point where homologous chromosomes separate in meiosis I. Secondary spermatocytes and secondary oocytes (as well as first polar bodies) should therefore each have 20pg of DNA. After meiosis II the resulting nuclei should have 10pg each. If you understand events at interphase and in meiosis, this question is easy to answer. Carefully examine the figure below to understand events during the interphase as far as DNA content is concerned. Then examine F2.3 in this book to see how chromosomes are behaving in meiosis. From this information you should see the answers as follows:

Primary spermatocyte = 40 pg
First polar body   = 20pg
Secondary oocyte   = 20pg
Ootid (in G_1)   = 10pg

It might be helpful to view changes in DNA content in graphic form:

Primary
oocyte

Secondary
spermatocyte

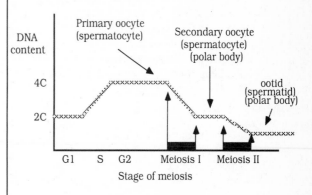

The "C" stands for "complements" of DNA.

(c) If the mosquito is heterozygous for the recessive gene *wavy bristles* (*wb*) then it would have the genotype *Wb/wb*. Because there are four letters here representing the two genes, the slash between the symbols helps us to understand that there are only two genes being discussed.

We are asked to draw an acrocentric, mitotic metaphase chromosome complement in this heterozygous insect. We are expected to place the gene symbols on the chromosomes. Recall that there is no synapsis of homologous chromosomes in mitotic cells, therefore, the chromosomes should not be placed side-by-side. Since sister chromatids are *identical* and homologous chromosomes are *similar*, we should draw the figure as follows:

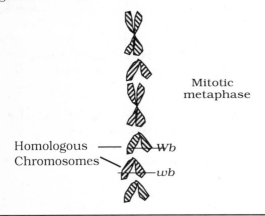

Mitotic
metaphase

Homologous
Chromosomes

Wb

wb

Common errors:
  incorrect number of chromosomes
  incorrect chromosome morphology
    metacentric, acrocentric
  poor relationship of DNA
    content to cells
  inappropriate symbols
  inappropriate placement of genes

Ch.2 Ques.9 (a,b) Recall that a metacentric chromosome has "arms" of approximately equal length, while submetacentric and acrocentric chromosomes have arms of unequal length.

Metaphase I (Primary Oocyte): homologous chromosomes are replicated and synapsed. There will be two X chromosomes present because oocytes occur in females. On the metacentric chromosomes (#1), place *Dd*., such that sister chromatids are identical. Place the **+** - alternatives on the X chromosomes.

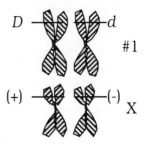

First Polar Body: the first polar body is a product of meiosis I, after homologous chromosomes have migrated to opposite poles. At this stage, dyads are present. Because females produce polar bodies, there should be an X chromosome present. Because the female is heterozygous, there are several possible answers. Note that there is only one representative of each allele for each gene pair. One possibility

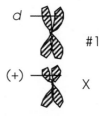

Secondary Spermatocyte: a secondary spermatocyte will have the same chromosome configuration as a First Polar Body. Both are products of meiosis I and dyads should be present. Because spermatocytes occur in males, there will either be an X chromosome or a Y chromosome present. There are, therefore, two possible answers. Regarding the genetic constitution of these cells, as stated in the problem, we are to assume that the male is Rh⁻ and **+** for the G6PD locus. Since this locus is on the X chromosome, only one genotype (regarding the X chromosome) can be presented.

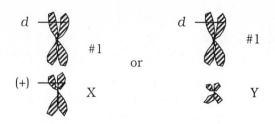

Secondary Oocyte: being a product of meiosis I, dyads will be present. Because oocytes occur in females, there should be an X (not a Y) chromosome present. The genetic labeling pattern for the secondary oocyte will be the same as for the first polar body.

One possibility

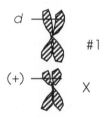

(c) If a G$_1$ nucleus contains 6.5pg DNA, then the following DNA contents are expected.

Metaphase I (Primary Oocyte):	13pg
First Polar Body:	6.5pg
Secondary Spermatocyte:	6.5pg
Secondary Oocyte:	6.5pg

Common errors:
   incorrect number of chromosomes
   incorrect chromosome morphology
      metacentric, acrocentric
   poor relationship of DNA content
      to cells
   inappropriate symbols
   inappropriate placement of genes

Ch.2 Ques.10 **(a)** Since the cell contains only two chromosomes (2n=2) and there are two chromosomes pictured, it cannot represent a cell in the second phase (II) of meiosis. The chromosomes are telocentric, which means that the centromere is at the end of the chromosome. When pulled at anaphase, two sideways "**V**s" or "**< >**" would be expected and the cell would be at the anaphase stage of meiosis I. The only other possibility to produce the "**< >**" figure would be a metaphase chromosome at anaphase of mitosis or anaphase II of meiosis. However, these possibilities are negated because the chromosomes are stated as being telocentric.

(b) In order to get the correct answer for the second part one must consider that, because of the S-phase, at anaphase I the DNA complement is twice that of a G$_1$ cell. Therefore, the correct answer is 16pg DNA.

Common errors:
   confusion on:
      significance of *telocentric*
      significance of chromosome
         number
   many students consider the
      chromosomes to be metacentric

Chs.2,4 Ques.11 **(a)** The female parent would have the following labeled chromosomal symbolism remembering that at meiotic metaphase I, chromosomes are doubled, condensed, and synapsed.

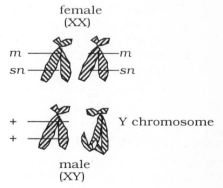

(b) In general, mitotic metaphase chromosomes are not synapsed, although in *Drosophila* mitotic chromosomes do pair. To avoid confusion and to be consistent with what is expected in other organisms, the mitotic chromosomes will not be drawn in the paired state.

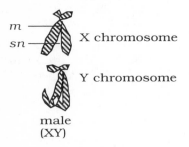

X chromosome

Y chromosome

male
(XY)

(c) All of the female offspring from the above cross should be heterozygous and phenotypically wild type. The one exceptional female could have resulted from maternal nondisjunction at meiosis I or II, thus producing an egg cell with two X chromosomes, each containing the *sn* and *m* genes. When fertilized by a sperm cell carrying the Y chromosome (along with the normal haploid set of autosomes) an $X^{sn\ m}X^{sn\ m}Y$ female is produced.

(d)

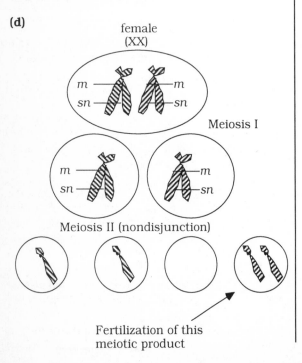

female
(XX)

Meiosis I

Meiosis II (nondisjunction)

Fertilization of this meiotic product

Common errors:
 incorrect chromosome morphology
  X, Y chromosmes
 inappropriate symbols
 inappropriate placement of genes
 problems with meiotic nondisjunction

Ch.2 Ques.12 (a) Since the chromosome numbers are given in *pairs*, recall that during meiosis each gamete contains one chromosome of each pair. If the red fox has 17 pairs of chromosomes, then each gamete will contain 17 chromosomes. For the Arctic fox, each gamete should contain 26 chromosomes. A zygote is produced from the union of the parental gametes, therefore it should contain 43 chromosomes (17 + 26). It turns out that some such hybrids are viable but usually sterile because of developmental and chromosomal alignment and segregational problems at meiosis.

(b) If G_1 nuclei contain 12pg and 8pg DNA, then the gametes produced from these organisms will contain 6 and 4pg DNA respectively. Combining these gametes gives 10pg for a G_1 cell. For a G_2 cell there should be 20pg DNA.

Common errors:
 confusion with *pairs* of
  chromosomes
 gametic chromosome number
 confusion with uneven number of
  chromosomes
 confusion with *somatic* cells

Chs.3,4 Ques.13

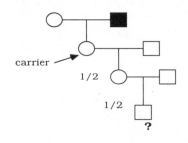

carrier

1/2

1/2

?

Because the maternal grandfather was colorblind, the woman's mother is a carrier for this X-linked gene ($X^{Rg}X^{rg}$). The woman therefore has a 1/2 chance of inheriting the X^{rg} chromosome from her mother and a 1/2 chance of passing this X^{rg} chromosome to her son. The chance that the son will receive the X^{rg} chromosome is therefore 1/4 (1/2 X 1/2). However, the question asks for the probability that the son will be normal.

The answer is, therefore, 1 minus 1/4, which equals 3/4.

> **Common errors:**
> **difficulty in setting up pedigree**
> **inability to see independent**
>   **probabilities**
> **multiplication of independent**
>   **probabilities**
> **seeing that the *normal* is requested**

Chs.3,4 Ques.14 (a) First one must determine whether the gene for *tan body* is X-linked or autosomal (not on the sex chromosome). Because half of the F_2 males are mutant and half are wild type, and all the females are wild, the gene for *tan body* is behaving as X-linked. The F_1 female is heterozygous, therefore she should have either of the alleles (t, t^+) on the one X chromosome (a secondary oocyte has one representative of each chromosomal pair) in the following arrangement. Because *Drosophila* has 8 chromosomes, each secondary oocyte should have four chromosomes (including the X chromosome).

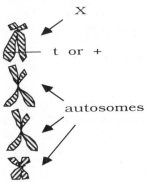

(b) A primary spermatocyte has the chromosomes in a doubled, condensed, and synapsed state. A tan-bodied male should have an X (containing a t gene) and Y chromosome as well as a diploid complement of autosomes.

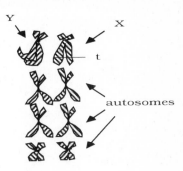

> **Common errors:**
> **difficulty in recognizing X-linked**
>   **inheritance**
> **problems with placing genes on**
>   **chromosomes**
> **problems with visualizing genome**

Ch.3 Ques.15 First, assign gene symbols:

G = gray, gg = white

(a) Since there is an approximate 1:1 ratio in the progeny, the parental genotypes are Gg X gg.

(b) A 3:1 ratio is apparent, therefore the parental genotypes are Gg X Gg.

(c) Because there are no gray phenotypes and *gray* is the dominant allele, the parental genotypes must be gg X gg.

(d) Since there are no white types and the sample is sufficiently large, it is very likely that the parental genotypes are GG X gg.

> **Common errors:**
> **students usually have only minor**
>   **problems with this type of**
>   **question**
> **some careless, random mistakes**

Chs.3,4 Ques.16 Set up the crosses with an appropriate symbol set such as the following:

h = hemophilia
H = normal allele
$I^A I^B$ = AB blood group
$I^o I^o$ = O blood group

Group A.

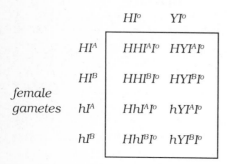

male gametes

	HI^o	YI^o
HI^A	$HHI^A I^o$	$HYI^A I^o$
HI^B	$HHI^B I^o$	$HYI^B I^o$
hI^A	$HhI^A I^o$	$hYI^A I^o$
hI^B	$HhI^B I^o$	$hYI^B I^o$

female gametes

Collecting phenotypes gives:

1/4 female, normal, A blood (200)
1/4 female, normal, B blood (200)
1/8 male, normal, A blood (100)
1/8 male, normal, B blood (100)
1/8 male, hemophilia, A blood (100)
1/8 male, hemophilia, B blood (100)

Group B. In this example the forked-line method will be used. Consider what will be happening for the *hemophilia* locus independently from the blood group locus.

1/4 females, normal —— 1/4 A blood (50)
2/4 AB blood (100)
1/4 B blood (50)

1/4 females, hemophilia – 1/4 A blood (50)
2/4 AB blood (100)
1/4 B blood (50)

1/4 males, normal —— 1/4 A blood (50)
2/4 AB blood (100)
1/4 B blood (50)

1/4 males, hemophilia – 1/4 A blood (50)
2/4 AB blood (100)
1/4 B blood (50)

Common errors:
difficulty with any dihybrid situation
X-linked with autosomal inheritance
incomplete dominance
calculating frequencies
observed numbers

Ch.3 Ques.17 (a) An appropriate null hypothesis for this example would be that the observed (measured) values do not differ significantly from the predicted ratio of a 1:1:1:1. One might also say that any deviation between the observed and predicted values is due to chance and chance alone.

(b) Because there are four classes being compared, there will be three degrees of freedom.

(c) Given that the Chi-square value of 20.00 is considerably greater than 7.82 (for three degrees of freedom) the null hypothesis should be rejected and the conclusion should be that the observed values differ significantly from the predicted values based on a 1:1:1:1 ratio.

Common errors:
inability to see a 1:1:1:1 ratio
development of the expected ratios
interpreting probability values
from table

Chs.2,4,5 Ques.18 In order for this type of fly to occur, the zygote must start out as a heterozygote in which both mutant genes are on one homologue and wild type alleles are on the other. In addition, one of the wild type chromosomes must get "lost" at the first mitotic division, thus making the female half $X^{+\ +} X^{w\ sn}$ and the other half $X^{w\ sn}$ O. The diagram below explains this situation.

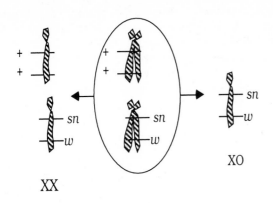

XX   XO

Because XX nuclei produce female tissue and XO nuclei produce male tissue, the phenotypes of the two sides are thus described. Developmentally, once the cleavage nuclei reach the peripheral areas of the egg to form a blastoderm, they become committed to their adult fate. Because there is little "wandering" of nuclei either during their migration to the egg periphery or after they reach the periphery, the male/female boundary is quite clean.

Common errors:
  difficulty in setting up the problem dealing with mitotic nondisjunction embryonic development of
    Drosophila

Chs.2,3,6 Ques.19 At the *molecular level* one could consider that in discontinuous inheritance the gene products are acting fairly independently of each other, thereby providing a 9:3:3:1 ratio in a dihybrid cross for example. Genotypic classes

$$A\_B\_, \ A\_bb, \ aaB\_, \ \text{and} \ aabb$$

can be clearly distinguished from each other because the gene products from the *A* locus produce distinct influences on the phenotypes as compared to those gene products from the *B* locus. Exceptions exist where epistasis and other forms of gene interaction occur. In discontinuous inheritance, one would consider each locus as providing a *qualitatively* different impact on the phenotype. For instance, even though the *brown* and *scarlet* loci interact in the production of eye pigments in *Drosophila*, each locus is providing qualitatively different input.

In continuous inheritance, we would consider each involved locus as having a quantitative input on the production of a single characteristic of the phenotype. In addition, although it may not always be the case, we would consider each gene product as being qualitatively similar. Under this model, the *quantity* of a particular set of gene products, influenced by a number of gene loci, determines the phenotypic characteristic.

At the *transmission level* one sees "step-wise" distributions in discontinuous inheritance but "smoother" or more bell-shaped distributions in continuous inheritance as shown in the figure below. For instance, in a dihybrid situation (*AaBb* X *AaBb*) where independent assortment holds, one would obtain a 9:3:3:1 ratio (assuming no epistasis, etc.) under a discontinuous mode but a 1:4:6:4:1 where genes (or gene products) are acting additively (continuous inheritance). Both patterns are formed from normal Mendelian principles of segregation, independent assortment, and random union of gametes. It is the manner in which the genes (or gene products) interact which distinguishes discontinuous from continuous inheritance.

Common errors:
   difficulty with "molecular level" of the question
   confusion over differences and similarities relating discontinuous and continuous patterns

---

Chs.2,8 Ques.20 The basis of the solution is to recall that crossing over occurs at the "four-strand stage" (after the S-phase) and each chiasma involves only two of the four chromatids present in each tetrad. Therefore, for each chiasma only two of the four, or 1/2, of the chromatids are crossover chromatids.

Gene mapping basically is the process of dividing the number of crossover chromatids by the total number of chromatids. Since each chiasma involves only two of the four chromatids, the map distance must be half of the chiasma frequency. If there are 18 map units between two genes then the chiasma frequency would be 36%. If one examined 150 primary oocytes, one would therefore expect to see 0.36 X 150, or 54 cells with a chiasma between the two loci.

Common errors:
   problem seeing relationships chiasma, map units
   problems "seeing" meiosis
   visualization of crossing over

Ch.8 Ques.21 The key to solving these types of "reverse mapping" problems is to keep in mind that a map unit is computed by the equationn and that if the map distance is given it is easy to determine the percentages of parental and cross-over offspring. Remember that there are two classes of crossovers and two classes of parentals from each cross.

(a)

$$AB/ab = 40\%, \; ab/ab = 40\% \; \text{(parentals)}$$

$$Ab/ab = 10\%, \; aB/ab = 10\% \; \text{(crossovers)}$$

(b) $AB/ab = 50\%, \; ab/ab = 50\%$ (all parentals)

The reason that there are all parentals and no crossovers in this cross is that there is no crossing over in male *Drosophila*. With no crossing over, the AB/ab chromosomes in the male are passed to gametes without crossovers.

Common errors:
   difficulty in going from map units to frequencies of classes of offspring
   failure to see that there are two parental and two crossover classes
   minor, careless mistakes

Ch.8 Ques.22

See the explanation for Question 21 above.

Notice that this is independent assortment.

(a) $Pq/pq = 25\%, \; pQ/pq = 25\%$ (parentals)

$PQ/pq = 25\%, \; pq/pq = 25\%$ (crossovers)

(b) $DB/db = 50\%, \; db/db = 50\%$ (all parentals)

Chs.9,10, 11, 14 Ques.23 (a) DNA replicates in a semiconservative manner such that each daughter strand is "half-new" and "half-old" in a particular pattern.

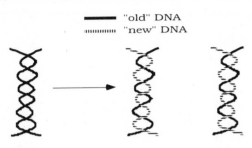

(b) The *Central Dogma of Biology* is based on the production (through transcription) of an RNA messenger from a DNA template and the subsequent "decoding" of that messenger by the process of translation.

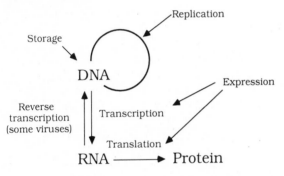

(c) The DNA template contains a sequence of nitrogenous bases which specifies a code from which amino acids are ordered in proteins. Through tautomeric shifts and a number of other natural factors (radiation, chemicals), changes can occur in that sequence of bases. Indeed, the mechanisms by which genes replicate themselves generate errors and leaves us with the conclusion that DNA is an inherently unstable molecule.

(d) Given the variety of organisms and the variation within organisms, there must be numerous, hundreds of millions, elementary factors which are inherited. DNA can provide for this variety by differences in the length and sequence of bases for each inherited functional unit. Given that there are four different types of bases, a sequence having merely ten bases would be capable of 4^{10} (over 1 million) different sequences.

Common errors:

There are usually very few problems with this type of question, except that students often have difficulty clearly explaining that which they know in model form. Written descriptions tend to be more lists of examples rather than explanations of structures and/or processes.

Chs.10 Ques.24 As discussed in the text, the rate of reassociation of melted DNA increases as the proportion of repetitive DNA increases. Such relationships are reflected in C_0t curves in which one plots the fraction of DNA reassociated against a logarithmic scale of C_0t values which have the units (mole X sec/liter). Because denatured DNA strands which are repetitive have a higher likelihood of complementary interaction, the time of reassociation is less.

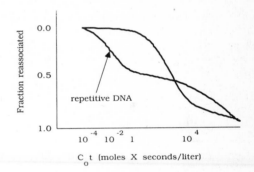

Common errors:
**orientation (coordinates) of graph
significance of curve components
repetitive DNA fraction
unique fraction**

Chs.10, 11 Ques.25 (a) In this type of drawing, the various carbons of the sugar are readily apparent. It is the orientation and carbon numbering on the sugar which determines the 5'-3' orientation of the molecule. The bottom of the polymer has the 2' and 3' carbons projecting, while the top has the 5' carbon projecting. Therefore, the bottom, near the circle is the 3' end of the molecule.

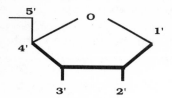

(b) Notice that there is no vertical line protruding from the 2' carbon position in the drawing and that uracil (U) is present. The molecule must therefore be an RNA. **(c)** It is best to start this portion of the problem by roughly drawing the complementary strand, remembering that it will be antiparallel.

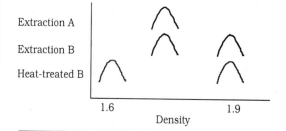

If it is a DNA complement, it will have thymine in place of uracil. There is no indication as to the complementary strand being RNA or DNA. Since all ATP's (or dATP's) have at their innermost phosphate a ^{32}P, make certain that they are properly labeled as given below. Since spleen diesterase cleaves between the phosphate and the 5' carbon, the 5' neighbors (C, T or U) will be labeled with the ^{32}P.

(d) Since snake venom diesterase cleaves at the 3' position (between the phosphate and the 3' carbon), the originally labeled ATP (or dATP) will retain the label.

Common errors:
5' to 3' orientations
labeling of complementary strand
understanding enzyme cleavages

Ch.11 Ques.26 Even though circular, in the context of this question, DNA from *E. coli* can be viewed in the following manner. Replication will occur semiconservatively and give the following sedimentation profile.

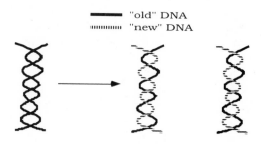

The heat treatment will cause the double-stranded structures to separate, giving the following strands and the profile as shown above.

Common errors:
confusion with the labeling experiment
difficulty in seeing sedimentation profiles
application of semiconservative replication

Chs.10,11 Ques.27 **(a)** There will be two telocentric metaphase chromosomes in the drawing and each chromatid will be labeled.

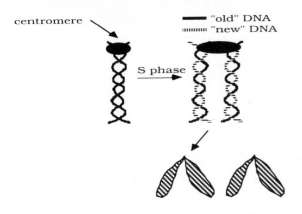

centromere

——— "old" DNA

.... "new" DNA

S phase

This autoradiographic pattern results because of semiconservative replication. Any cell which contains labeled chromosomes will have had its chromosomes pass through an S phase in the presence of label.

(b) Consider that the DNA was labeled with a dCTP having the innermost phosphate labeled. As this triphosphonucleoside is incorporated into the DNA, it will have the following relationship to its neighbors. *Snake venom diesterase* cleaves DNA at the 3' position meaning that it breaks the bond between the phosphate and the 3' carbon.

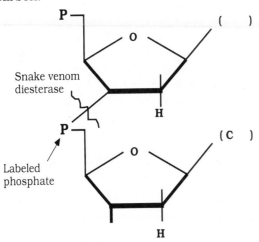

P

O

( )

Snake venom diesterase

H

P

(C)

O

Labeled phosphate

H

Therefore, the labeled phosphate remains attached to the 5' carbon of the cytosine nucleotide. The A+T/G+C ratio of 1.67 is of no consequence in answering this problem because all of the label remains attached to the cytosine.

Adenine_____   Guanine_____

Thymine_____   Cytosine _100%_

Common errors:
inappropriate labeling pattern
inability to draw telocentric
chromosomes
understanding cleavage at
3' position
eliminating extraneous
information

Ch.11 Ques.28 1. This must be the *5' end* of the polymer because all synthesis of polymers is 5' to 3' and the head of the arrow is at the other end of the polymer.
2. The *leading strand* is that strand which is synthesized continuously.
3. A *DNA ligase* will join the nicks.
4. The *lagging strand* is the discontinuous strand.
5. The free end that is complementary to the 5' end at arrow #1 must be the 3' end. That being so, the complement to that 3' end would be 5'. Therefore the *5"end* is at arrow #5.
6. A *helicase* is involved in unwinding the DNA helix.
7. An *RNA primer* is synthesized to initiate DNA synthesis.
8. *DNA gyrase* functions to remove supercoils generated by unwinding the DNA helix.
9. *Single-stranded binding proteins* stabilize the template which is to be replicated.

Common errors:
determination of 5', 3' polarity
naming of enzymes involved

Ch. 12 Ques. 29 Overall, this is a drawing of simultaneous transcription and translation in which the RNA polymerase is moving from right to left, making an mRNA which is complementary to one of the two strands of DNA. Ribosomes have added to the nascent (newly forming) mRNA and what appear to be polypeptide chains are protruding from the ribosomes.

(1, 2) In answering this question, remember that all synthesis of nucleic acids starts at the 5' end and finishes at the 3' end. Therefore, immediately label the end near point "B" with a 5'. The projecting strand is the nascent mRNA. Recall that all orientation of complementary strands is antiparallel and since the RNA polymerase is going from right-to-left (according to the arrow) the end of the DNA strand from which the mRNA is copied is the 3' end. Now, since the 3' end of the DNA template strand is identified, its DNA complementary end (at point "A") must be the 5' end.

(3) The codon-anticodon relationship is also antiparallel (based on hydrogen bonding) and since the 5' end of the mRNA is identified, letter "C" must be at the 5' end.

(4) While the diagram is *not to scale*, given the folded structure of the molecule and its position in the ribosome, consider the RNA nearest to letter "D" as tRNA.

(5) Remember that the 3' end of the tRNA holds the amino acid, therefore letter "D" is where the amino acid would be attached.

(6) The tRNA binds mainly to the large subunit of the ribosome, while the mRNA binds mainly to the small subunit of the ribosome. The question asks for the S value of the rRNA in that small subunit. Simultaneous transcription and translation occurs in prokaryotes only (not eukaryotes). The S value for the small subunit of a prokaryotic ribosome is 30S but that value includes both rRNA and protein. The rRNA molecule however has an S value of 16, which is the correct answer.

(7) Since all of the ribosomes are moving along the same mRNA, the amino acid sequences are the same. Therefore, the amino acids nearest the letters "F" and "G" are the same.

Common errors:
  polarity of DNA and RNA strands
  structure of ribosomes
  overall understanding of translation

Chs. 13, 14 Ques. 30 One of the most frequent difficulties students have with this problem is remembering that the code is triplet and three bases in the mRNA code for each amino acid in a protein. The 5' end of the mRNA corresponds with the N-terminus of the amino acid chain.

(a) Transition mutations will cause amino acid substitutions. Counting over by "threes" from the N-terminus, the amino acid *ile* should be altered.

(b) Inserting a base between positions 3 and 4 will change the second amino acid; however, recall that acridine orange is a frameshift mutagen and insertion of a base will alter the reading frames for all "downstream" amino acids. Therefore, all amino acids in positions 2 (glu) through 12 will be influenced (excluding degeneracy).

(c) Nitrous acid causes base substitutions, therefore a mutation in the 11th base would influence the amino acid *leu*.

Common errors:
  counting amino acids as bases
  not understanding what base changes
  do to amino acid sequences

Chs.,13,14 Ques.31 Notice that there are two mutant strains (cannot grow on minimal medium) and one wild type strain (t410). The best way to approach these types of problems, especially when the data are organized in the form given, is to realize that the substance (supplement) which "repairs," as indicated by a (+), a strain is after the metabolic block for that strain. In addition, and most importantly, the substance which "repairs" the highest number of strains either *is the end product* or is *closest to the end product.*

Looking at the table, notice that supplement *B* "repairs" both the mutant strains. Therefore, it must be at the end of the pathway or at least after all the metabolic blocks (defined by each mutation). Supplement *A* "repairs" the next highest number of mutant strains (1), therefore it must be second from the end. The pathway, therefore, would be as follows:

```
              t409        r3
Precursor----\---->A ----\---> B
```

To determine the locations at which the strains block the pathway through mutation, apply a similar logic. A block that is "repaired" by all the supplements must be early in the pathway. A block which is "repaired" by only one supplement must be late in the pathway. A supplement which does not "repair" a strain is before that strain's metabolic block.

> **Common errors:**
> **inability to construct a pathway**
> **failure to see how additives "repair"**
>   **mutant phenotypes**
> **difficulty in assigning metabolic**
>   **blocks in pathways**

Ch.13 Ques.32

1. Hydrophobic cluster formed by interaction of hydrophobic amino acids.

2. α helix formed from hydrogen bonds between components of the peptide linkage.

3. Covalent, disulfide bonds formed between cysteine residues

4. The polar amino acids will tend to orient to the outside of the protein where the charged R groups will interact with water.

> **Common errors:**
> **nature of hydrophobic clustering**
> **understanding of α and β structures**
> **polar side chains and hydrophilic**
>   **interactions**

Chs.15 Ques.33 Any time a regulatory protein interacts with DNA and transcription is stimulated, it is called *positive* control. Any time a regulatory protein interacts with DNA and represses transcription it is called *negative* control. In completing the chart, apply these simple rules.

Relationship of Regulator Protein to DNA	Operator	
	Positive control	*Negative control*
is bound	**on**	**off**
isn't bound	**off**	**on**

> **Common errors:**
> **confusion with positive and negative control**
> **confusion with repressible and inducible systems**

Chs. 15 Ques.34 In some viruses, overlapping genes present a mechanism for providing two and sometimes more protein products from a single stretch of DNA. In eukaryotes, different sets of introns may be removed, thus providing for a variety of protein products from a single section of DNA. This process is often called *differential splicing*.

> **Common errors:**
>
> **Students often have difficulty in orienting *specific information* they have learned to a general question. If asked about overlapping genes, or differential hnRNA splicing, they would be able to develop an answer. Students sometimes confuse overlapping genes with the non-overlapping code.**

Chs.15, 16 Ques.35 DNase is a general term which includes a variety of exo- and endonucleases which cleave DNA from the ends or internally, respectively. Such cleavage is often irrespective of base sequence. If naked DNA is exposed to DNases, it is rapidly degraded to oligo- and mononucleotides. When protein is associated with DNA, it protects regions from degradation. Such protected regions can be analyzed as to base content. Restriction endonucleases cleave DNA at specific sequences often hundreds or thousands of base pairs apart. If one is interested in mapping protein binding sites, one would want to use an enzyme (a DNase) with frequent yet relatively random cleavage characteristics, not restriction endonucleases.

> **Common errors:**
> **understanding overall strategy differences between**
> **DNases**
> **restriction endonucleases**

Ch. 16 Ques.36 Notice that the fragment sizes (in kb) on the left side of the figure match the *Hind*III restriction fragments which are hybridizing (cDNA probe + genomic fragment) to the radioactive probe. Each band therefore represents a region where the radioactive probe is "trapped" by complementary base pairing to single-stranded DNA fragments which are bound to the filter. The smaller fragments migrate faster in the gel and therefore are in the bottom portion while the larger fragments are at the top, near the origin.

Notice that the intensity of the bands from the normal individual is somewhat uniform, indicating that all the restriction fragments are found in equal amounts. However, the intensity of three of the bands from the patient with retinoblastoma are about half as dense as in the normal. One band (7.5 kb) has the same intensity as in the normal.

Because humans are diploid organisms, with normally two copies of each gene, one may hypothesize that the individual with retinoblastoma has a heterozygous deletion of a portion of the retinoblastoma gene which includes *Hind*III fragments (9.8, 6.2, and 5.3 kb). It is likely that the inheritance of such a deletion is instrumental in causing familial retinoblastoma.

> **Common errors:**
>   **understanding of experimental design**
>   **cDNA probes**
>   **Southern blots**
>   **electrophoresis**
>   **restriction endonuclease analysis**
>   **hybridization**
>   **recognition of deletion**

Ch. 16 Ques.37 Below is a drawing of the expected product if either of the above plasmids (A) or (B) is restricted to completion with *Bam*HI. There should be a 2.3 kb fragment (1.4 + 0.9 kb) and the remainder (9.2 - 2.3 = 6.9). Notice that the 6.9 kb fragment migrates slower (higher in the gel) than the 2.3 kb fragment. Also notice that the intensity of the stain is less in the smaller band because there is less DNA to bind the stain.

(a)

(b) To distinguish between the (A) and (B) orientations, one could make use of the change in position of the *Pst*I restriction site in the two orientations. First, estimate the number of kb in the two fragments resulting from *Pst*I restriction of orientation (A). Notice that in orientation (A) the *Pst*I fragments are approximately 2.4 (1.4 for the *Kan* gene + about 1.0) kb and 6.8 kb. In orientation (B) the sizes would be approximately 1.9 (0.9 for the *trx* gene + about 1.0) and 7.3 kb. With appropriate standards, these size differences could be distinguished on agarose gels.

> **Common errors:**
>   **electrophoretic analysis**
>   **restriction enzyme analysis**
>   **experimental design**

Chs.16 Ques.38 It is a relatively simple procedure to determine the sequence of DNA from the gel given. Start at the bottom with the smallest fragments. As one reads up the gel, one is reading from the 5' to the 3' direction. In the first case, note that there is a band in both the G+A and G lanes. Read this as a "G" because if an "A" occurs, it would exist as a band *only* in the G+A lane. The sequence would be as follows: 5'-GTGGTCACGACT

> **Common errors:**
>   **reading the gel as the sequence**
>   **difficulty in dealing with G+A**
>   **and C+T lanes**
>   **careless mistakes**

Ch. 16 Ques. 39 The dideoxynucleotide method of sequencing takes advantage of the absence of a 3' OH group on the ribose sugar. Polymerization is dependent on extension from that 3' OH. When mixing in a ddNTP chain growth stops. Because the investigator controls the addition of a given ddNTP, he/she knows at which base termination has occurred. Thus, a pouplation of DNA fragments is generated in which the terminal base of each is known. By separating the fragments by electrophoresis, the investigator can determine the length of each of the terminated fragments and therefore the position of each base.

In the gel, the sequence is read from the bottom up: TTCGTGAAGAAT

> **Common errors:**
> Difficulty in seeing how chain termination can provide informaition on gene sequences. Not understanding that gel electrophoresis can separate fragments as different as one base in length.

Ch. 17 Ques. 40 Viral and bacterial chromosomes are structurally distinct from those of eukaryotes. They usually consist of a single nucleic acid molecule (DNA in bacteria and RNA or DNA in viruses), unlike the multiple chromosomes of eukaryotes. Viral and bacterial chromosomes are largely devoid of associated proteins and contain relatively fewer, tightly packed, genes. Viral genomes can be single or double stranded, linear or circular nucleic acids. Bacterial chromosomes are always double stranded DNA and often associated with DNA-binding proteins, two called HU and H. These proteins are structurally similar to histones which are found in eukaryotic chromosomes.

In eukaryotes, genomes consisted exclusively of double stranded DNA with relativley large proportions not encoding typical protein products. Chromosomes contain histones which are relatively small basic proteins that form octomers called nucleosomes, around which DNA wraps. See the *Essentials* text for a detailed discussion of histones and chromosome structure.

> **Common errors:**
> This is a more descriptive question which requires students to merely learn the taxonomy of various chromosomes. There are very few conceptual issues here to cause problems.

Ch. 17, Ques. 41 Specialized chromosomes are found in eukaryotes and because of their size, and therefore utility, they often deserve special mention. Polytene chromosomes, discovered by Balbiani in 1881, are found in various tissues of fly larvae and several species of protozoans. Each chromosome contains 1000-5000 DNA strands in parallel register. Differences in DNA/protein packing generate linear bands or chromomeres. Local uncoiling results in a "puff" which is a visible manifestation of transcription.

Lampbrush chromosomes were discovered in 1892 in oocytes of sharks and are now known to be characteristic of most veterbrate oocytes as well as the spermatocytes of some insects. They are meiotic chromoosmes which contain lateral loops composed of a DNA double helix actively involved in transcription.

> **Common errors:**
> This is a more descriptive question which requires students to merely learn various chromosome types. Students often just forget about these historically useful chromosome types.

Ch. 18 Ques. 42 (a) An antibody molecule contains two identical light (L) chains and two identical heavy (H) chains. There are two classes of L chains and five classes of H chains. Variability results from variability in the genes encoding the chains and recombination among genes making up each chain.

(b) L : 300 V X 10 J = 3,000, H: 300 V X 10 D X 10 J = 30,000.

(c) Total molecular variation: 3,000 L X 30,000 H = 9 X 10^7

> **Common errors:**
> **source of variability**
> **general antibody structure**
> **randomness of recombination**
> **careless computation**

Ch. 18 Ques. 43 A proteome defines the complete set of proteins expressed and modified during a cell's lifetime. Proteomics, the study of the proteome, uses technologies ranging from genetic analysis to mass spectrometry. The goal for proteomics is to provide for each protein encoded in a genome an informational set which includes function, structure, modifications, localization, variants, and evolutionary relationships. To increase the speed and accuracy of proteome analysis, scientists are using DNA chip technology.

> **Common errors:**
> **Difficulty in remembering this**
> **new branch of molecular/cell**
> **biology and what its goals include.**

Ch. 19 Ques. 44 Somatic gene therapy is the transfer of genes into the somatic cells of an individual. This type of therapy is done with the permission and informed consent of the patient. In germ line therapy, the sex cells are genetically altered, thus altering the entire genetic makeup of the individual for all future generations. Such research is presently prohibited. Another type of gene therapy, enhancement gene therapy, is conducted with the goal of enhancing human performance.

> **Common errors:**
> **Difficulty in remembering the three**
> **individual classifications. No con-**
> **ceptual problems here.**

Ch. 19 Ques. 45 (a) Several additional problems in the study of human genetics would include the following.

1. With a relatively small number of offspring produced per mating, standard genetic methods of analysis are difficult.

2. Records on family illnesses, especially behavioral illnesses, are difficult to obtain.

3. The long generation time makes longitudinal (transmission genetics) studies difficult.

4. The scientist cannot direct matings that will provide the most informative results.

5. The scientists can't always subject humans to the same types of experimental treatments as other organisms.

(b) With the relatively late age of onset of Huntington's disease, an individual may have children with Huntington's disease, thus indicating the presence of the gene, but die of other causes (accident, military, *etc.*) before the disease manifests itself. A pedigree having incomplete penetrance will result.

(c) With twin studies, one can readily compare the differential influences of genetic make-up and the environment. Monozygotic twins have the same genetic makeup but can be reared under different environmental conditions if the twins are separated for one reason or another. Dizygotic twins have a different genetic makeup but because they are the same age (almost) they are often reared under fairly uniform conditions within a family. Given these "experimental" advantages, the genetic contribution to certain diseases can often be estimated.

(d) *Genetic background.* While it is often difficult to assess the influence of genetic background on gene expression, many genes are influenced by "modifiers" which enhance or suppress expression. Since each individual gene functions within an environment produced by all other active genes of the genome, it is reasonable to expect that a host of "background" factors will influence the expression of a gene. Such background factors may involve positional as well as molecular/developmental factors.

Environment and *general health.* The physical and behavioral environment in which an individual is raised will influence the degree to which a particular genotype is expressed. Seeing it another way, what may be acceptable or normal behavior in one environment may be abnormal in another. When a living system is stressed by disease or other factors, the chemical/physiological state of the organisms is altered. It is expected that such alterations would be reflected in various behaviors.

Nutrition. The raw materials used in growth and maintenance of the living state are usually provided by the diet. As nutrients fluctuate, changes will be expected in the metabolic state of the organism. Such changes may influence a series of biochemical reactions involved in the expression of a gene. Certain traits are influenced by the metabolic state of the individual and such traits may be influenced by nutrition.

> **Common errors:**
> **Difficulty in relating concepts from different chapters in the text**
> **Confusion over penetrance and expressivity**

Ch.20 Ques.46 *Determination* is a significant, complex, yet poorly understood process whereby the specific pattern of genetic activity is initially established in a cell. This pattern will direct the developmental fate (differentiation) of that cell. *Differentiation* is the process of cellular expression of the determined state. It is the complex series of genetic, morphological, and physiological changes which characterize the variety of adult cells.

(b) *Determination* occurs before *differentiation*. In *Drosophila*, determinative events are thought to occur about the time of blastoderm formation, when nuclei encounter the peripheral regions of the egg. *Differentiation* of most of the adult cells occurs during metamorphosis, some five to six days after embryogenesis (determination).

DETERMINATION

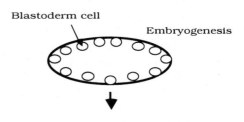

Blastoderm cell

Embryogenesis

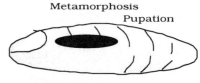

Metamorphosis
Pupation

DIFFERENTIATION

> **Common errors:**
> **providing accurate definitions**
> **failure to relate determination and differentiation to each other temporally**

Ch.20 Ques.47 The *variable gene activity hypothesis* of differentiation acknowledges the genomic equivalence of cells within an organism and assumes that of all the genes in a given cell type, only certain ones produce products while the others are shut down and are not transcribed. As shown below, certain genes will be active in all cells, those *housekeeping* genes coding for vital cellular functions, while others will be differentially regulated in various cell types. Differential gene transcription occurs in both spatial (different cells of an organism) and temporal (different times during development) dimensions.

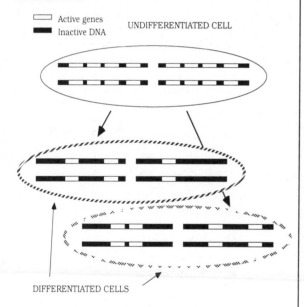

Support for this model is provided by several observations and experiments.

1. *Chromosome puffs:* Specific puff patterns, representing differential gene activity, are observed in dipteran polytene chromosomes at different times during development.

2. *Isozymes:* Differential gene activity is demonstrated by the observation that different forms of the same enzyme (isozymes) are present in cells of different tissues. This evidence assumes that such isozyme patterns are not caused by post-transcriptional forms of genetic regulation.

3. *Growth hormone: In situ* hybridization and immunochemical studies in mouse embryos demonstrates spatial and temporal aspects of the regulation of growth hormone transcripts in the anterior pituitary gland.

Common errors:

With a general question such as this, students sometimes have difficulty focusing on the area in their notes or in the text which relates to the question. Students may understand what is meant by the *variable gene activity hypothesis* but not immediately see that it relates to the question. Students also have difficulty in relating a variety of experimental findings to a general theme.

Ch.22 Ques.48 Since 8% of the males express the trait and males have only one X chromosome, the frequency (q) of the recessive gene would be .08 and p would be .92. Since females have two X chromosomes, the expected frequency of females that are homozygous for the color blindness gene would be q^2 or .0064 (.64%).

The frequency of females that are heterozygous would be $2pq$ or $2(.08)(.92) = .1472$ or 14.72%.

Because the population is in equilibrium, the frequency of men with color blindness will not change from generation to generation. Eight percent of the men will be color blind in the next generation. Students should be aware of many deviations of these types of questions. The basic scheme is the Hardy-Weinberg equilibrium and the equations which apply.

> **Common errors:**
> application of the Hardy-Weinberg
>   equations to a sex-linked gene
> failure to apply the Hardy-Weinberg
>   equations in determining the
>   frequency of heterozygous
>   females
> students often make the question
>   harder than it is by forgetting
>   that under equilibrium
>   conditions, gene frequencies
>   do not change

> **Common errors:**
> failure to provide a complete list
> failure to briefly and adequately
>   describe each term
> failure to see that inbreeding
>   does not, in itself, change
>   gene frequencies

Ch.22, 23 Ques.49 *Mutation*, while being an original source of genetic variability, is not usually considered to be a significant factor in changing gene frequencies.

Migration occurs when individuals move from one population to another. The influence of migration on changing gene frequencies is proportional to the differences in gene frequency between the donor and recipient populations. Organisms often migrate as a result of some stress. Those organisms suffering from the most stress are often those that leave. Therefore, they do not represent a random sample of the individuals in that home range.

Selection can be a significant force in changing gene frequencies. It results when some genotypic classes are less likely to produce offspring than others. Selection may be directional, stabilizing, or disruptive.

Genetic drift can be a significant force in changing gene frequencies in populations that are numerically small or have a small number of effective breeders. In such populations, random and relatively large fluctuations in gene frequency occur by "sampling error."

Inbreeding is not a significant factor in changing gene frequencies in populations, however, it will change zygotic or genotypic frequencies. The number of homozygotes will increase at the expense of the heterozygotes.

Ch.23 Ques.50 Reproductive isolation can occur because of the introduction of geographic barriers or other dramatic changes in the environment which subdivide a population. Such factors facilitate speciation because gene flow is eliminated or at least restricted. With gene flow restricted, isolated populations can experience changes in gene frequencies when the Hardy-Weinberg assumptions are *not* met. Under Hardy-Weinberg equilibrium conditions where there is *random mating, no genetic drift, no selection, no mutation,* and *no migration*, gene frequencies will remain the same and speciation will not occur.

> **Common errors:**
> confusion as to what the question
>   is asking
> difficulty in relating information
>   from one chapter to information
>   contained in a different chapter

Ch.24 Ques. 51 In small populations the chance of inbreeding, matings between closely related individuals, increases, thus increasing the proportions of homozygotes in a population. With that increase in homozygosisty, there is an increased possibility that an organism may be homozygous for a deleterious allele (inbreeding deppression). Outbreeding depression occurs where reduced fitness results from progeny between genetically diverse individuals. Offspring may be less well-adapted to the local environmental conditions in which their parents survived..

> **Common errors:**
> explanations of terms
> general relationships between these
>   two forms of breeding depression